THE S

CW00411156

Other Titles of Interest

Preface

Many of the inventions made over the last hundred years have been superseded by more up to date inventions which out perform their predecessors. The vinyl disc is one which gave very good service over many years, but now it has given way to cassette tapes and the compact disc. Another example is the valve which has given way to the transistor and then the integrated circuit.

There are a few ideas which will remain with us for many years to come. One of these is the superhet radio. It has formed the basis for most radios since the 1920s. Now over seventy years later there are no other ideas even on the horizon which might replace it.

Today a vast number of radio applications utilise the idea of the superhet radio. Domestic radios of all descriptions as well as cellular phones and many professional applications all use the superhet principle. When it was first invented, those involved could not have conceived of its usage today.

With its importance in current radio and electronics technology it was felt that a book about its principles and the various parts of a superhet radio would be of interest to the radio and electronics enthusiast.

Ian Poole

Contents

Chapter 1

INTRODUCTION AND HISTORY

Almost without exception, every household in Great Britain owns at least one radio. Most have several, ranging from ordinary transistor portable radios to Walkmans, stereo cassette radios, hi-fi tuners and car radios. Their popularity proves that radio has become an integral part of our everyday lives. As a result we have come to take them for granted and expect even the cheapest sets to give a very high level of performance.

Radio sets are expected to perform a number of functions. Primarily they should amplify signals to the right level and accept only the wanted one, rejecting others on adjacent channels. To fulfil these requirements, a type of radio called the superhet is used in virtually all types of radios from the cheapest portable sets right up to the most expensive professional communications receivers.

Invented in the First World War, the superhet first gained popularity in the early 1920s and 1930s. Since then it has remained in constant use. During this time valves have given way to discrete transistors, which in their turn have bowed to integrated circuits. Yet despite all these changes the superhet principle has remained the same even though radios of today are far more complicated than the early ones, offering much better performance and many more facilities.

The Arrival of the Superhet
The invention of the superhet represents the results of many years work by a wide variety of people. Many observed new effects or made discoveries which they thought would have uses elsewhere. However each one fitted another piece into the jigsaw which made the superhet possible.

One of the earliest discoveries was made by an American named Fessenden. He made a discovery which was fundamental to the operation of the superhet. At the time morse signals would be heard in the headsets of the operators as a series of clicks which could easily be confused with atmospheric noise. Fessenden had the idea of transmitting a signal which would

1

produce the required sound in the headset. To do this he proposed transmitting two signals together which were close in frequency. When detected by the receiver this would appear in the headset as an audio tone which would be much easier to copy. This idea was patented in 1901.

Having established the basic principle, Fessenden refined it. Realising that the transmission of two signals used twice as much power and equipment, he suggested that only one signal should be transmitted. The other one should be generated in the receiver itself, and this would give the operator the flexibility to control the pitch of the beat note to give the best readability under the given conditions.

Fessenden called the oscillator in his receiver a heterodyne oscillator from the two Greek words heteros and dynamis, meaning external force.

Like many engineers, Fessenden was ahead of his time and the technology was not available to utilise his ideas. As a result no further development took place for a number of years.

It was not until 1913 that sufficient progress had been made to implement the heterodyne principle satisfactorily. In this year the U.S. Navy undertook some tests which proved that a heterodyne receiver gave the best results of any system available at the time.

Whilst the basic heterodyne principle was being established a number of other discoveries were being made. One of the most far reaching was the thermionic valve. Its discovery not only enabled radio receiver technology to progress, but it also laid the foundations of modern day electronics.

The first effects leading to the thermionic valve were noticed by Edison. He was investigating methods of extending the life of light bulbs. One of the factors reducing their life was the blackening which occurred on the inside of the glass bulb. To overcome this, he placed a second electrode in the bulb and applied a negative potential to it. When he did this Edison noticed that current flowed in one direction between the filament and the new electrode, but not in the other. Whilst Edison was fascinated with this new discovery which he called the Edison Effect, he never found a use for it.

It fell to Dr J. A. Fleming, the professor of electrical engineering at University College London to put this idea to use.

Fleming had acted as a consultant to Marconi in his experiments with long distance communications. It was in fact Fleming who designed the transmitter and much of the other equipment which was used to make the first transatlantic radio transmission in 1901. Fleming realised that the major weakness in any radio system of the time was in actually detecting the signal in the receiver. He thought that the Edison Effect which he had seen a few years earlier might provide a solution. Accordingly he set up an experiment to investigate this, and he quickly proved that the idea worked and provided a detector which was far superior to anything else which was available at the time. As a result the thermionic valve was born in 1904.

Fleming's diode valve was followed two years later by the triode. This was invented by an American named Lee de Forest, and although the third electrode had been added the device was still only used as a detector. It took a number of years before it was realised that it could also be used as an amplifier.

With the use of valves as amplifiers it was quickly discovered that they could also be made to oscillate. In fact the first reliable oscillators were made in 1913 by Telefunken. This was a major step forwards because previous sources of sine waves were very cumbersome and expensive.

Initially very little was really understood about the way in which valves operated. As more was learned about them, the rate at which advancements were made increased. Many new types of receiver started to appear. A brilliant young American named Edwin Armstrong made the first regenerative set. This gave greatly increased gain and selectivity over anything else which was available.

In another development a British radio engineer called H. J. Round developed a receiver called the autodyne. In this set a single valve was made to perform as oscillator and mixer at the same time. This was a great advantage because of the high cost of valves and the difficulties encountered in supplying current to a large number of them. All supplies were provided by batteries, and each valve required its own filament supply. As the filaments often drew an amp or more the sets were not cheap to run.

As these advances were made a further ingredient was added which fuelled developments even more. In 1914 the First World

3

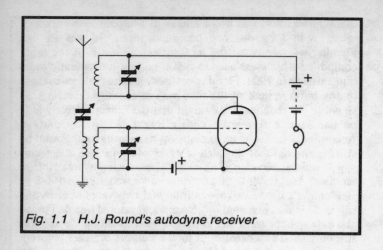

Fig. 1.1 H.J. Round's autodyne receiver

War broke out. With this the value of radio communications was soon appreciated and a great impetus was given to the development of improved equipment.

During these very early days of radio development, most of the transmissions were made on frequencies below 500kHz. Great difficulties were encountered above this because valve amplifiers had very little gain owing to the limitations of the valves available at the time. In addition to this the interelectrode capacitance meant that circuits suffered badly from instability. Many people tried to overcome these problems, and a degree of success was achieved. Even so it was obvious that a completely different approach was needed.

The first major step was taken by a French engineer named Lucien Levy. His main interest was in achieving greater levels of selectivity. To do this he developed the idea of converting the incoming signals to a lower frequency where they could be tuned and separated from one another more easily. He accomplished this by mixing the incoming signals with another fixed frequency oscillator generated locally in the receiver. This produced what he called an "ultra-acoustical" beat to give signals at a lower frequency. The mixer was then followed by a tuned stage with an amplifier before the signals were converted to audio by the use of a second heterodyne oscillator.

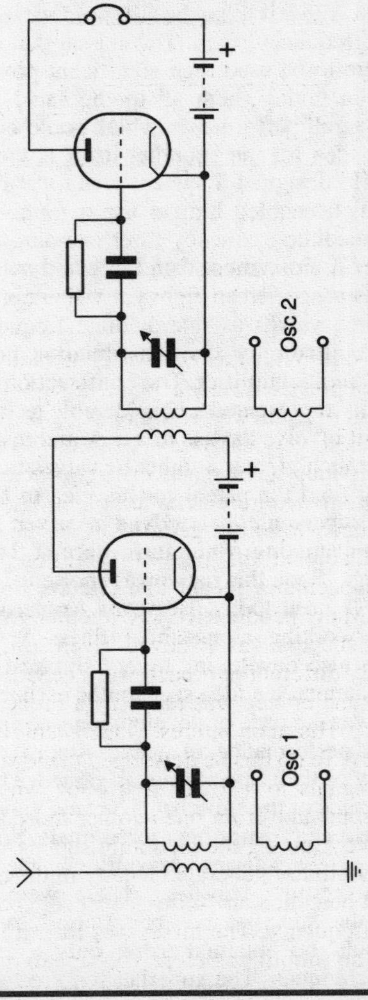

Fig. 1.2 Lucien Levy's idea for a receiver with a mixer and intermediate frequency selectivity

Levy's system worked well, although it could not remove all the atmospheric noise as he claimed it would. With greatly improved selectivity and a higher gain the idea gave a marked improvement. As a result he patented the idea in 1917.

Although Levy had very nearly discovered the idea of the superhet as we know it today he still used variable tuning at the intermediate frequency stage. This meant that if several stages of tuning were to be used then significant problems would be encountered in tuning them all to the same frequency. This limited the overall performance which could be achieved.

The basic idea for the superhet itself is credited to Edwin Armstrong. He designed a system using a variable frequency oscillator which enabled him to use a multi-stage fixed frequency intermediate frequency filter and amplifier. This gave an even larger improvement than Levy had noticed. In his first receiver Armstrong used an eight valve line up: 1st mixer, local oscillator, three valves as intermediate frequency amplifiers, heterodyne oscillator for the demodulation process, and two valves in the audio amplifier. The construction of a receiver of this complexity represented a considerable technical challenge. Not only did it involve the use of a new and revolutionary idea, but it used a much greater number of valves than other sets.

Armstrong filed the patent for his idea in December 1918, calling it a supersonic heterodyne receiver because of the heterodyning or mixing which took place at frequencies above the audio range. Soon this name was shortened to superhet, the name which is used today. However Armstrong was not the only person working along these lines. A German named Schottky was also developing a very similar type of receiver, and he had patented his idea six months earlier.

After the war the pace of developments seemed to slow only slightly. The performance of valves improved as a greater understanding of their operation was gained. This eroded many of the advantages of the superhet. The new valves enabled high gain radio frequency amplifiers to be made, and as there were comparatively few stations transmitting, the need for high degrees of selectivity was less. There were other practical reasons for the superhet not being used. A sufficient performance could be obtained using only a few valves with traditional techniques. The superhet required a larger number

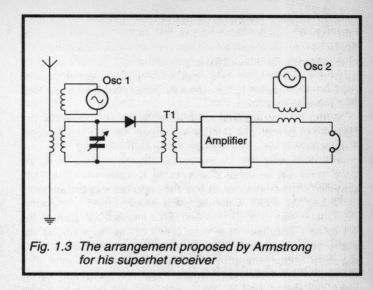

Fig. 1.3 The arrangement proposed by Armstrong for his superhet receiver

of valves, some of which did not contribute to the overall gain of the set. This meant they were more expensive, and less attractive to manufacture or buy.

In view of these problems comparatively little was heard about the idea for a number of years. However in the U.S.A. the number of high power broadcast stations began to rise in the late 1920s. This meant that the need for a higher degree of selectivity was again needed. Unfortunately a number of problems still needed to be overcome before the superhet could enjoy any degree of widespread use.

The early sets had suffered from a very poor image response because they used a very low intermediate frequency (often 50kHz as standard) to enable the best performance to be achieved from the valves. Now the improvements in valve technology helped the superhet. As a result the standard inter-mediate frequency became 180kHz. In addition, the new "dull emitter" valves consumed much less filament current, reducing the cost of buying and running the sets.

Problems still remained with tuning. Two controls were needed, one for the variable local oscillator and one for the radio frequency stage. As both controls had to be adjusted correctly this made the sets more difficult to use and sell. The problem was overcome by the development of a dual gang variable capacitor in which two capacitors could be varied in line with one another on one spindle. All these developments enabled the superhet to become a variable type of set to be used in the domestic market.

With the superhet well established in the U.S.A., it did not take long before its popularity began to rise in Europe. Particularly in the 1930s when more high powered broadcast stations began to start broadcasting. Just as in the U.S.A. the need arose for sets which were able to cope with the more crowded band conditions. Again the superhet was the answer.

During the 1930s a number of new ideas were introduced. Automatic gain control was one. This enabled the gain of the set to be controlled for a wide range of inputs, enabling the audio volume control to be kept almost constant for a wide range of signal strengths. Further improvements were also made in valve technology. Smaller and more efficient valves were introduced, and the performance of the sets was gradually improved. In fact many of the sets made in the 1930s give quite acceptable performance today.

The Second World War gave a further impetus to improving the design of radios. Although no changes were made to the basic concept, refinements were made so that the selectivity, sensitivity, and stability were all made much better.

The next major revolution to the superhet occurred after the invention of the transistor. Being much smaller and requiring less current they enabled portable sets to become quite commonplace. Some valve portable sets had been manufactured using special valves which consumed less filament current and used lower anode voltages. However they were never very popular because they needed expensive high voltage batteries, which did not last very long.

The first transistor portables became available in large quantities in the early 1960s. Since then integrated circuits have been incorporated into domestic sets even more. Using the increased functionality available in these chips performance has improved quite considerably. In addition to this, features like entering the frequency from a keypad on the front of the set, memories to store the frequencies of favourite stations and many more have become commonplace.

The scanner, a new type of set which is able to scan a band of frequencies or selected channels has become very popular to the amateur listener. These and many more developments have ensured that the future of the superhet remains in no doubt for many years to come.

Chapter 2

BASIC PRINCIPLES

In the previous chapter it was mentioned that the heterodyne or mixing process is crucial to the superhet radio. In this process the receiver converts the incoming signal on one frequency to a fixed intermediate frequency where it can be filtered and amplified far more easily and effectively. However before proceeding with a more detailed description about the actual workings of the superhet itself it is best to look at how the mixing or heterodyne process works.

Mixing
The basic function of a radio frequency mixer is to change a signal from one frequency to another by mixing it with a second signal. As a result of its action this type of circuit is sometimes described as a frequency changer.

This type of circuit should not be confused with an audio mixer. This piece of equipment is used in a wide variety of applications to add together sounds from different sources. Music groups needing to add sounds from several microphones and instruments will use a mixer as will radio stations and many other users. However the type of circuit used in additive mixers is totally different to the mixers used for frequency changing.

It is possible to illustrate how a frequency changing mixer works by using a simple illustration. Musicians use the effect to tune their instruments to the same frequency. If two musical notes close together in pitch are heard at the same time then the sound will appear to become louder and softer as the notes reinforce one another and then cancel each other out. The rate at which the reinforcement and cancellation occurs is called the beat frequency and it is equal to the difference in frequency between the two signals. When there is no pitch difference the beat note will not be heard, and this will occur when both instruments are in tune, i.e. on exactly the same frequency.

In order to produce a similar effect and mix signals together electronically a circuit which has the effect of multiplying the two signals together is used. At any instant the output of the circuit will be proportional to the levels of the two inputs multiplied together. When a circuit which can accomplish this is used, a beat note will be produced which will be equal to the difference between the two input signals.

In addition to this another signal is produced. This has a frequency equal to the sum of the two input signals. In other words if the two input signals have frequencies of f_1 and f_2 then two new signals will be produced at frequencies of $(f_1 - f_2)$ – the difference or beat frequency and $(f_1 + f_2)$ – the sum frequency.

The effect of mixing can be shown graphically as shown in Figure 2.1. Here the two signals can be seen at the top of the diagram, and below the resultant signal can be seen. If this is examined it can be seen that this new signal has a component at a low frequency (the difference or beat frequency), and another one at a much higher frequency (the sum frequency).

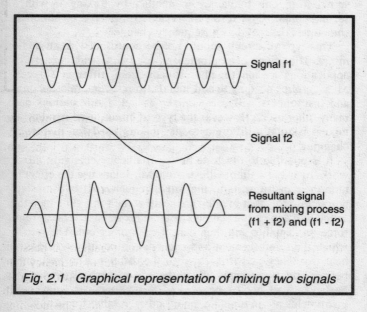

Signal f1

Signal f2

Resultant signal from mixing process (f1 + f2) and (f1 - f2)

Fig. 2.1 Graphical representation of mixing two signals

It is also possible to give a diagram of the spectrum of the signals involved in the mixing process. Figure 2.2 shows the process from this point of view.

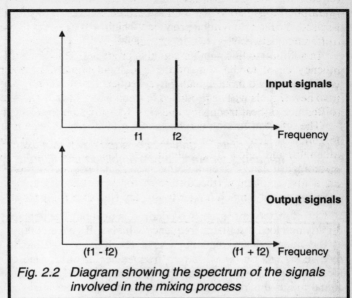

Fig. 2.2 *Diagram showing the spectrum of the signals involved in the mixing process*

It is also possible to express this mathematically. If two sine waves $\sin\theta_1$ and $\sin\theta_2$ are mixed, they will produce two signals $\sin(\theta_1 - \theta_2)$, the difference frequency, and $\sin(\theta_1 + \theta_2)$, the sum frequency, i.e.:

$$\sin\theta_1 \times \sin\theta_2 = \sin(\theta_1 + \theta_2) + \sin(\theta_1 - \theta_2)$$

The Superhet Radio
It can be seen that by mixing two signals together it is possible to produce signals which are lower or higher in frequency than the original ones. This idea can be used to convert the signals in a radio from one frequency to another, by mixing them with a second signal from an internal local oscillator. The incoming signals are converted to a fixed frequency intermediate frequency stage where they are amplified and filtered as shown in

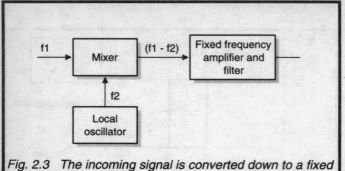

Fig. 2.3   The incoming signal is converted down to a fixed frequency where it can be amplified and filtered

Figure 2.3.

Unfortunately there are two conditions or input frequencies for any one local oscillator frequency which will give an output at the intermediate frequency. As a result it is possible to receive signals on two different frequencies at once. One of these signals is generated as the difference of the incoming signal minus the local oscillator frequency. The other arises as the difference between the local oscillator minus the incoming signal.

To illustrate this it is useful to take some real figures to act as an example. If the intermediate frequency stages with their filter are at 500kHz and the local oscillator is running at 1500kHz then it can be seen that a signal on 2000kHz (i.e. 2000 – 1500kHz) will produce a signal at 500kHz. Similarly a signal at 1000kHz (1500 – 1000kHz) will also produce a signal on 500kHz.

It is obviously no use to be able to receive signals on two totally different frequencies at once. Only one signal must be received and the unwanted one, called the image signal must be rejected. To achieve this a simple filter is placed before the mixer as shown in Figure 2.4. This can be designed to accept or reject either signal. As the filter only has to reject the image signal, and not those on adjacent channels, it can be relatively simple. It does not need the same degree of selectivity required by the filter in the intermediate frequency stage.

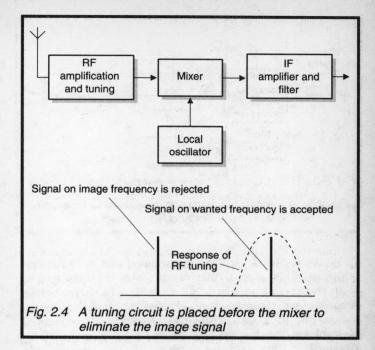

Fig. 2.4 *A tuning circuit is placed before the mixer to eliminate the image signal*

Tuning

So far the description of the superhet has been confined to the fixed frequency case. However in most applications it is necessary to tune the radio over a band of frequencies. Even an ordinary Medium Wave portable radio will need to tune over a fairly wide band, and short wave radios or scanners will tune over even wider bands.

Tuning is primarily accomplished by altering the frequency of the local oscillator. In the example of the receiver with an intermediate frequency of 500kHz and a local oscillator frequency of 1500kHz, signals were received on 1000kHz. If the local oscillator is moved up in frequency by 100kHz to 1600kHz, this mean that signals are received 100kHz higher up. This maintains the 500kHz difference between the local oscillator and incoming signal frequency.

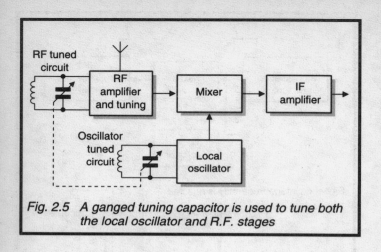

Fig. 2.5 *A ganged tuning capacitor is used to tune both the local oscillator and R.F. stages*

Whilst the local oscillator is the main part of the circuit which has to be altered, other circuits have to be changed as well. The filtering prior to the mixer needs to be altered to take account of the frequency change. If this is not done then the circuit may be off tune and cause the wanted signal to be reduced in level and the unwanted image signal to be increased. To overcome this the pre-mixer or radio frequency tuning should track or tune at the same rate as the local oscillator. In receivers using analogue tuning, i.e. a dial and tuning knob, this is accomplished by having a ganged variable tuning capacitor with two or more sections.   One section is used to tune the local oscillator and the other remaining sections (often only one) are used to tune the radio frequency stages as shown in Figure 2.5.

Basic Superhet
A block diagram of a typical basic superhet radio is shown in Figure 2.6. More complicated radios with additional features and better performance specifications will undoubtedly be more complicated and have more stages. Some sets will have two or more conversion stages. However an explanation of the working of an overall superhet radio can be gained from this basic block diagram.

16

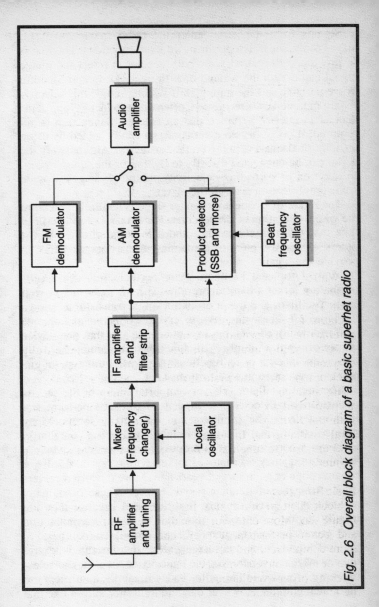

Fig. 2.6 Overall block diagram of a basic superhet radio

17

Signals from the aerial enter the radio frequency or r.f. stages of the set which perform two main functions. The first is to provide the required selectivity needed to reject the image signal and accept the wanted one. In many Long and Medium Wave portable sets the tuning coils which provide this selectivity are mounted on a ferrite rod, often about 6 inches long. This acts as an internal aerial so that an external connection is not required. If necessary an external aerial can be added by using an additional small winding on the ferrite rod. Alternatively the aerial can be connected directly to the top of the tuned circuit. In addition to providing selectivity many r.f. stages provide some amplification prior to the mixer.

The mixer of frequency changer stage is naturally crucial to the whole operation of the receiver. The mixer circuit itself can take many forms, containing diodes in some circuits, whilst others are active circuits containing transistors or FETs to provide some gain.

Many Long and Medium Wave portable sets use a self-oscillating mixer which incorporates the r.f. functions as well as the oscillator and mixer around a single transistor as shown in Figure 2.7. These circuits are very cost effective and operate well in low priced sets, but in view of the fact that one device is performing a number of functions it cannot be fully optimised for each of its functions. As a result this type of circuit is never found in a performance set.

The local oscillator is a very important item in the set. Its performance will determine aspects of the set's performance including drift. The oscillator can take many forms. Many radios use a free running variable frequency oscillator. However where low drift is required, other systems where a variable frequency oscillator is mixed with a crystal oscillator became popular a number of years ago. More modern receivers often make use of frequency synthesizers. These offer many advantages in terms of very low drift and because they are usually digitally controlled they can be used in conjunction with processors to give memory, scan and search facilities.

The output from the mixer enters the intermediate frequency stages. It is here that the majority of the gain and selectivity are provided in the radio. Today many i.f. amplifiers use integrated circuits. However discrete transistor stages like that

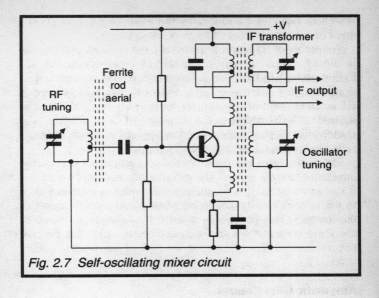

Fig. 2.7 Self-oscillating mixer circuit

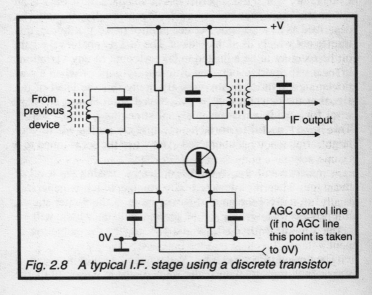

Fig. 2.8 A typical I.F. stage using a discrete transistor

shown in Figure 2.8 still are found in many sets. This gives a good idea of the function of one of these stages.

A number of standard frequencies have been adopted for use in the i.f. stages of radios. 465kHz is very popular for AM radios whilst 1.6MHz used to be quite common in communications receivers some years ago. 9MHz is now widely used in HF amateur radio equipment (for operation below 30MHz). For Broadcast VHF FM sets the standard i.f. is 10.7MHz. The choice of i.f. depends upon a number of factors which are more fully covered in Chapter 4 – Selectivity.

Once the signal has been filtered and amplified it is still in the form of a radio signal. The modulation needs to be removed from the carrier to give an audio signal which can be amplified in the normal way before being passed into a loudspeaker or headphones. This process is called demodulation or detection, and there are a number of different circuits which can be used to perform this depending upon the type of transmission being used.

Automatic Gain Control

One feature which the superhet has as standard these days is an automatic gain control (a.g.c.). Occasionally it may be described as an automatic volume control (a.v.c.), although this term is not widely used these days. The facility enables the gain of the receiver to be adjusted to take account of any variations in level which occur between different stations, or when a particular signal varies in strength. By doing this the level of the signal at the detector can be maintained at an almost constant level for a wide variation in signal strengths from the aerial. This is very useful in portable sets, and car radios where very large variations are encountered even when the set is tuned to a fixed station.

In essence an a.g.c. system operates by sensing the level of the signal when it is detected. The voltage which is generated is used to control the gain of one or more of the earlier stages. The greater the signal, the larger the voltage which will be applied to the earlier stages and the greater the reduction in gain.

The design of a good a.g.c. system can be quite involved. It should not start to reduce the gain of the receiver until the signal has reached a sufficiently high level to give a good signal-to-noise ratio.

In addition to this the time constant must be taken into account. It is important that none of the audio modulation should be present on the a.g.c. control line. If this happens the a.g.c. will follow the level of the modulation and as a result it will tend to remove the audio. To ensure that this does not happen a simple filter is included and as a result there is always an associated time constant. For a.m., a time constant of about a quarter of a second is typical and this enables the control voltage to follow the average level of the carrier, taking into account any variations in overall signal strength.

For s.s.b. and morse transmissions the situation is slightly different because there is no constant carrier level which can be monitored. Instead the level of an s.s.b. signal will vary according to the amount of modulation present, falling to zero when there is no sound. Morse transmissions also consist of a varying level as the carrier is turned on and off. For an a.g.c. system to be able to cope with these types of transmission a longer time constant is needed. In fact they should quickly reach the required level when a new signal appears (the attack time), but hold this value for a while during speech pauses or gaps in the transmission for morse (the decay time). Typically an attack time of 0.1 seconds and a decay time of around a second or more will be quite satisfactory for most applications.

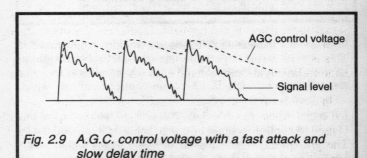

Fig. 2.9   A.G.C. control voltage with a fast attack and
         slow delay time

To generate the voltage for the a.g.c. a simple diode detector like that shown in Figure 2.10 is often used, especially in simple Medium Wave portable radios. Here the same diode is used for detecting the audio as well as generating the a.g.c. control voltage. The difference is that a much longer time constant filter is used for the a.g.c. A small amount of filtering is applied to the audio, simply to remove any of the radio frequency signal which may be present. In more sophisticated radios a separate detector can be used with its own final i.f. amplifier stage. In this way the a.g.c. detector can be properly optimised for this function.

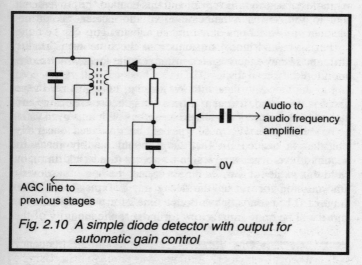

Fig. 2.10 A simple diode detector with output for
automatic gain control

The control voltage is generally applied to more than one of the r.f. and i.f. stages. Often it is applied as in the typical amplifier stage shown in Figure 2.8, although i.c. amplifiers are often used today, and these will have gain control terminals which can be used for this facility.

In some instances the voltage is applied to the mixer, but this is not to be advised because it means that this circuit will not be operating at its optimum. Ideally it should be applied to several amplifier stages. The more stages which are controlled, the greater the range of control which can be obtained.

Other Configurations

So far only the basic superhet configuration has been outlined. Whilst many of the radios available in the shops today conform exactly to this format, there are many which have additional stages to give improved performance in various areas.

One of the major problems of radios conforming to the basic format is that they do not give sufficient rejection of the image signal. Although it is possible to make some improvements by increasing the front end selectivity, it is not always possible to achieve the figures which are required. If major improvements need to be made then the best option is to increase the difference between the wanted and image signals. This can be done by raising the intermediate frequency. It can be seen that the difference between the wanted signal and the image is twice the intermediate frequency.

Raising the i.f. brings with it a number of problems. In the first instance high frequency filters can be more expensive and they may also be less effective. Nowadays with improved technology, high frequency filters can be produced relatively cheaply, but before the 1970s it was a significant problem. As a result a two stage conversion process was adopted in many sets as shown in Figure 2.11. The easiest method of achieving this was to have a variable first local oscillator as shown in the diagram. Then a crystal controlled oscillator was used to convert the signals down to a lower i.f. where the majority of the selectivity was found.

Unfortunately this did not give the optimum frequency stability because the local oscillator was prone to drift. Using a variable frequency oscillator at this stage meant that several compromises had to be made in the design. In the first case it was likely to have to operate at a high frequency, a major factor in determining the amount of drift. Secondly it would have to be switched to enable it to cover all the required bands, and finally the circuit values could not be optimised to reduce the drift as it covered a wide band of frequencies.

A much better method is to use a crystal controlled first conversion as shown in Figure 2.12. This configuration formed the basis of many amateur band receivers in the 1960s and 1970s.

The advantage of this method is that the inherent stability of the crystal oscillator can be employed in the first oscillator.

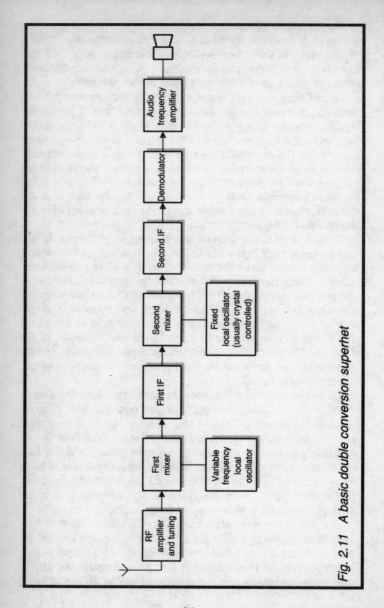

Fig. 2.11 A basic double conversion superhet

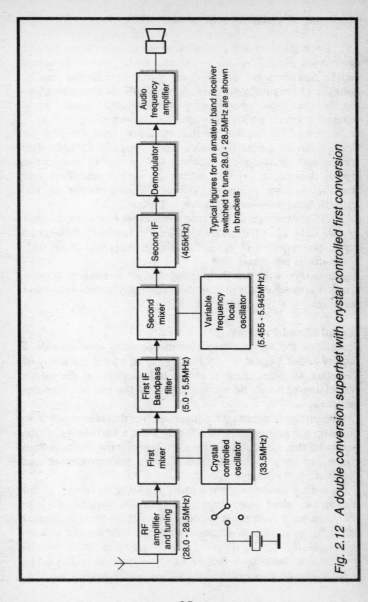

Fig. 2.12 A double conversion superhet with crystal controlled first conversion

Typical figures for an amateur band receiver switched to tune 28.0 - 28.5MHz are shown in brackets

RF amplifier and tuning (28.0 - 28.5MHz)

First mixer

First IF Bandpass filter (5.0 - 5.5MHz)

Second mixer

Second IF (455kHz)

Demodulator

Audio frequency amplifier

Crystal controlled oscillator (33.5MHz)

Variable frequency local oscillator (5.455 - 5.945MHz)

This type of circuit would remain stable despite the high frequencies, wide bandwidth and switched operation.

The variable frequency local oscillator is used for the second conversion. Here it is able to run at a much lower frequency, and because it is not switched the mechanical design can be optimised to ensure good stability. Normally receivers employing this technique operate very well, the drift having been reduced to levels which are normally not noticeable.

In view of the fact that the first oscillator is not variable, the first i.f. covers a relatively wide band, typically 500kHz. The second and variable local oscillator is then able to convert the signals down to a fixed i.f. where the normal selectivity and amplification are provided. Typical frequencies for an HF amateur band receiver are shown in Figure 2.12.

The disadvantage of this type of receiver is that as the first i.f. has only a limited bandwidth, a large number of switched bands are required if general coverage reception is needed. Often this is not practicable.

Nowadays with the widespread use of frequency synthesizers it is much easier to manufacture highly stable wide-band receivers.

Digital Signal Processing
Several of the top communications receivers now include a facility called Digital Signal Processing (d.s.p.). Like many of the other facilities used in radios today, some of the signal processing can now be accomplished by the use of computer technology.

The principle behind d.s.p. uses the fact that it is possible to build up a representation of a signal from a knowledge of the points on the waveform. If these are represented digitally then the waveform can be interpreted by a microprocessor and processed accordingly.

In a d.s.p. receiver the incoming signal from the i.f. is fed into an i.c. called an Analogue to Digital Converter (a.d.c.). In this chip the waveform is successively sampled and converted into a series of digital numbers, each representing the voltage at successive times. These samples are then used by the processor to build up a picture of the waveform which it can mathematically process in virtually any way. Filtering, amplification, and demodulation can all be accomplished.

Once processed the digital representation of the signal has to be reconverted back into an analogue form using an i.c. called a Digital to Analogue Converter (d.a.c.). It is then passed into an ordinary audio amplifier and a loudspeaker or headphones in the normal way.

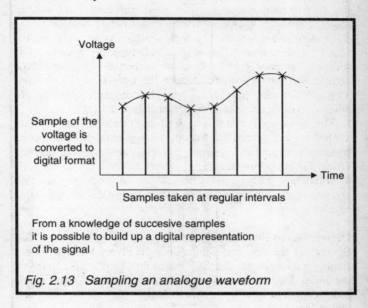

Fig. 2.13 Sampling an analogue waveform

The advantage of digital signal processing is that everything can be treated in a mathematical way. This enables signals to be treated far more exactly, and this gives many advantages including better filters, lower distortion during demodulation and the like. A further advantage is that new facilities can be added purely by changing the software.

As these processors become cheaper and the technology more accepted an increasing number of receivers will use d.s.p. in the years to come.

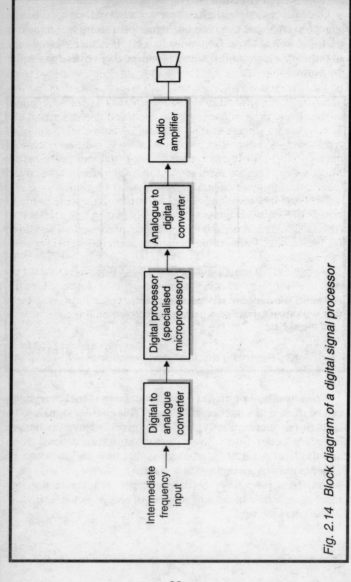

Fig. 2.14 Block diagram of a digital signal processor

Advantages of the Superhet

It is worth quickly summarising the main advantages of the superhet to show why it is so widely used. First and foremost is the selectivity. Even with today's advanced technology the superhet principle offers much better selectivity than any other type of receiver. The fixed i.f. enables very high quality crystal or other forms of filter to be used to give excellent performance. Ordinary tuned radio frequency (t.r.f.) receivers cannot approach the performance of even modest quality superhets.

Another advantage is that they can receive a wide range of types of modulation. Simply by switching in a different type of demodulator, a different type of modulation can be resolved. Many other types of receiver including the direct conversion receiver can only resolve a limited number of modes.

The superhet also lends itself to employing a wide range of types of facility. Having a fixed frequency i.f. a number of types of signal processing can be incorporated. Everything from advanced forms of noise limiter to digital signal processing can be used.

Against all of these advantages it must be agreed that superhets are more expensive than many other forms of radio. However as they are by far the most popular form, it is clear that the advantages far outweigh any cost penalties.

Chapter 3

SENSITIVITY AND OVERLOAD

One of the most important aspects of any radio is its sensitivity, or ability to pick up weak signals. Today's technology means that most receivers are very sensitive. This is illustrated by the fact that a modern communications receiver or scanner will be able to pick up signals which are less than a microvolt.

Unfortunately making a receiver sensitive is not the only aim of the designer. Simply adding further stages of amplification to make the set more sensitive can lead to overloading when strong signals are present. In many instances the ability of the set to accommodate a wide variation in signal strengths can be just as important. It is a challenge for a radio designer to make a set which can copy a very weak signal. It is even more of a challenge to design a radio which can copy the very weak signal if it is close to an exceedingly strong one.

However before looking at receiver sensitivity it is first necessary to look at the causes for the limiting factors.

Noise

Noise is the chief factor in limiting the sensitivity of receivers today. If noise did not exist there would be no problem in achieving sufficient levels of gain for the signals to be heard. Instead the background noise which arises from a number of sources can mask out the wanted signal. Obviously strong signals will not be affected by fairly low levels of noise, but the weaker signals can be partially or totally masked by it.

Noise consists of random electrical impulses spreading out over the radio spectrum. In many cases it is truly "white noise" which appears as a background hiss in the radio and is present at the same level over the whole of the radio spectrum. Other forms of noise may have a higher level at some frequencies than others. Some noise may even appear more as distinct signals, for example the pops and bangs which are often heard on the lower frequency bands.

Noise comes from two main areas. It can either be picked up by the aerial or generated within the receiver itself. Noise picked up by the aerial comes from a variety of sources. It may be man-made. With the variety of electrical and electronic equipment in use today this can be a major source of noise. Electric motors, televisions, cars, and even fluorescent lights all produce interference which can be picked up.

Atmospheric noise is also present. This mainly consists of "static" or impulses from the discharges of lightning in electrical storms. In view of the colossal amounts of energy released in these storms it is hardly surprising that they contribute noise over a wide area, dependent upon the propagation conditions at the time. Another source of noise comes from outer space. This cosmic or galactic noise comes from distant galaxies, but despite the distances it can be present in quite significant levels.

The level of all these types of noise varies with frequency. Some types of man-made noise can extend to very high frequencies. This is particularly true of ignition noise which can be detected quite easily from passing cars on domestic television sets at 400MHz and more. Other forms of man-made interference do not extend this high, often limited to somewhere between 5–10MHz. Atmospheric noise levels also fall with frequency leaving cosmic noise the main constituent above about 10MHz. This also falls in level as the frequency rises.

There are other forms of noise which are not picked up by the aerial. Thermal noise is of particular importance. It arises from the fact that there are free electrons available to carry current in any conductor. These electrons are in constant random motion, moving at a rate proportional to the temperature above absolute zero (–273°C). As the electrons are moving, albeit in a random fashion, this constitutes an electrical current. Although it is very small it can still be detected as random noise. It is also found that the level of the noise is linked to the value of the circuit resistance, and the bandwidth being used. This means that when a receiver input is connected to a 50Ω resistor, or even a 50Ω aerial a certain level of thermal noise will always be present.

Receiver design is fashioned to a large extent by the levels of noise picked up by the aerial. In view of the larger levels of noise entering the receiver from the aerial on the HF bands there is little point in designing receivers which generate exceedingly low levels of noise themselves. If this were done any noise from the aerial would totally mask any improvements seen in the receiver. However at frequencies above about 50 to 100MHz the levels of received noise fall to a point where noise generated in the set becomes the dominant factor. As this occurs more emphasis has to be placed on the design of low noise front ends.

In any receivers the noise performance of the front end stages is very important. Often the signals will be entering the receiver at levels which are comparable with the noise generated by the set. This noise is amplified along with the wanted signals. As a result any noise introduced at the front end will be amplified more than that generated in a later stage. To ensure that the maximum sensitivity is maintained, it is necessary to design front end circuits to introduce as little noise as possible.

Signal to Noise Ratio
The sensitivity of a receiver can be specified in a number of different ways. As we have seen noise can be the limiting factor in determining the weakest signals which can be heard. In view of this, the sensitivity of the set has to indicate the amount of noise

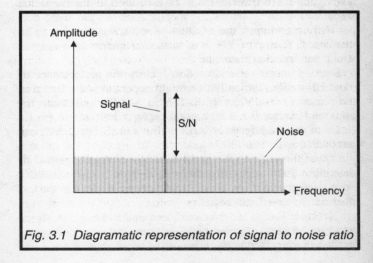

Fig. 3.1 Diagramatic representation of signal to noise ratio

generated by the set. The most obvious method of doing this is to specify the difference between the signal and the noise under specified conditions as shown in Figure 3.1. Obviously the greater difference between the unwanted noise and the wanted signal, the better the performance.

This difference between the wanted signal and the unwanted noise is usually expressed as a ratio between the signal and noise, i.e. a signal to noise (S/N) ratio and it is normally in decibels. As the level of the input signal obviously has an effect on this ratio, the input level needs to be specified as well. In other words the specification will give the specified signal to noise ratio for which the standard is usually 10dB for a given input level which is normally in microvolts (μV).

A number of other factors can affect the signal to noise ratio. One of these is the bandwidth which is used. It has been seen that noise spreads out evenly over the whole radio spectrum. This means that it is present at all frequencies, and the larger the bandwidth the greater amount of noise which will be picked up. In view of this the bandwidth used has to be quoted as part of the specification.

When using a.m. it will be found that the level of modulation has to be specified. This is done because the audio output level from the receiver needs to be measured to determine the signal and noise levels for the specification. As the audio output will depend upon the modulation level, this also has to be mentioned. A level of 30% is used as the standard for receivers which can resolve this mode.

Signal to noise ratio is used to specify the performance of most HF radios. Typically one might expect to see a figure in the region of 0.5μV for 10dB S/N in a 3kHz bandwidth for s.s.b. and morse. For a.m. a good receiver is likely to give a figure of around 1.5μV for 10dB S/N in a 6kHz bandwidth and a modulation level of 30%.

Whilst this may appear to be a very convenient method of determining and specifying the sensitivity of a receiver, there are a number of pitfalls. To see how these arise a look at the test methods involved can be taken. A basic set-up for measuring the sensitivity of a receiver is shown in Figure 3.2. A signal generator capable of accurately generating the very low signals needed is connected to the input of the receiver as shown.

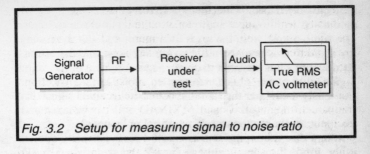

Fig. 3.2 Setup for measuring signal to noise ratio

With the generator signal switched off a 50Ω match is given to the receiver and the audio meter will detect the noise generated by the receiver itself. This level is noted and the signal turned on. Its level is adjusted until the audio level meter reads a level which is 10dB higher than just the noise on its own. The level of the generator is that required to give the 10dB signal to noise ratio.

The last statement was not strictly true. Whilst the first reading of the noise is quite accurate, the second reading of the signal also includes some noise as well. In view of this many manufacturers will specify a slightly different ratio: namely signal plus noise to noise (S+N/N). In practice the difference is not particularly large, but the S+N/N ratio is more correct.

Occasionally the signal generator level in the specification will mention that it is either p.d. or e.m.f. This is actually very important because there is a factor of 2:1 between the two levels. For example 1µV e.m.f. and 0.5µV p.d. are the same. The e.m.f. (electro-motive force) is the open circuit voltage, whereas the p.d. (potential difference) is measured when the generator is loaded. As a result of the way in which the generator level circuitry works it assumes that a correct (50Ω) load has been applied. If the load is not this value then there will be an error. Despite this, most equipment will assume values in p.d. unless otherwise stated.

SINAD

Another type of specification which is often seen, particularly where frequency modulation is used, is the SINAD measurement. In many respects this is very similar to the signal to noise ratio just described. The method involves applying a signal modulated with a single audio tone to the input of the receiver. The audio output from the set is then monitored and the resulting audio tone is notched out, leaving any noise and distortion. By doing this it is possible to obtain a measurement of the ratio: Signal plus Noise plus Distortion to Noise plus Distortion. Obviously the higher the ratio the better the received signal. To compare different sets a standard SINAD ratio can be taken and the input levels needed to achieve this can be noted.

Using this system the sensitivity of a set is normally quoted in the form of an input voltage (in μV) for a certain SINAD ratio expressed in dB. A figure of 12dB SINAD is normally chosen because this conveniently corresponds to a distortion factor of 25%.

Even though SINAD measurements are most commonly seen for f.m., there is no reason why the performance for other modes cannot be assessed using this system. For a.m. it is simply a matter of changing the type of modulation from f.m. to a.m. and then making the measurement in exactly the same way. For s.s.b., it is a little more difficult because tuning the receiver will introduce a frequency offset and this will mean that it can be more difficult to null out the original audio tone. However once this is done the measurement can be made in the normal way.

To give an example of the sort of figures which can be obtained a typical VHF set may be able to achieve a performance of around 0.2μV for 12dB SINAD.

Noise Factor and Noise Figure
For equipment used above 30MHz the signal to noise ratio is rarely quoted. Instead another system called the noise figure is widely used. This system is far more versatile and gives a better indication of the real performance of the equipment whether it is a complete receiver, a system, or just a pre-amplifier.

Essentially this measurement gives an indication of how much noise each stage introduces into the system. To understand how noise figure and factor work, take the case when a pre-amplifier input is terminated in a resistor of the same impedance as the aerial input. This will generate some noise which will be amplified by the amplifier. Any noise at the output over and above the level of the resistor multiplied gain of the circuit will have been introduced by the amplifier. The noise figure and noise factor quantify the amount of noise introduced by the stage.

The noise factor is simply the degradation of the signal to noise ratio as a result of it passing through the equipment. It can be determined by taking the signal to noise ratio at the input and dividing it by the signal to noise ratio at the output. As there is always some noise introduced by each stage the noise factor will always be greater than one.

$$\text{Noise factor} = \frac{\text{Signal to noise ratio at input}}{\text{Signal to noise ratio at the output}}$$

(N.B.: Signal to noise ratios expressed as a ratio and not in dB)

Noise factor is rarely seen in the specifications for receivers or other pieces of equipment. Instead the noise figure is used. In many respects the two figures are similar: the noise figure is simply the noise factor expressed in decibels.

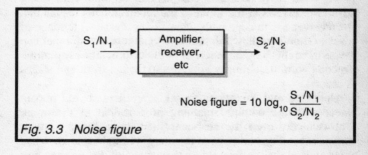

$$\text{Noise figure} = 10 \log_{10} \frac{S_1/N_1}{S_2/N_2}$$

Fig. 3.3   Noise figure

For example if the signal to noise ratio at the input was 4:1 and at the output it was 3:1, then this would give a noise factor of 4/3 and a noise figure of $10 \log_{10} (4/3)$ or 1.25dB. Alternatively if the signal to noise ratios are expressed in decibels then it is quite easy to determine the noise figure simply by subtracting the two figures because two numbers are divided by subtracting their logarithms. For example if the signal to noise ratio at the input was 12dB and at the output it fell to 10dB then the noise figure of the circuit would be 2dB (12 – 10).

The figures for different pieces of equipment will vary quite widely. An ideal piece of equipment would have a noise figure of 0dB as it would introduce no noise. Obviously this is not possible, but many pieces of equipment these days have a very good noise performance. A typical amateur radio VHF or UHF transceiver may have a noise figure of around 3dB, whereas a high performance preamplifier can have a noise figure of 1dB or slightly less. The noise figure of an HF receiver will be somewhat worse because the high level of noise picked up by the aerial means that any improvements will not be noticeable. Typically an HF receiver will have a noise figure between 10 and 15dB.

Large Signal Response
Whilst the sensitivity of a receiver is very important, it is not the only aspect of front end design which needs attention. On today's crowded radio spectrum there are many signals which can place very large voltages onto the input of a set using a good aerial. With a good receiving aerial many of the high power short wave broadcast stations can generate voltages of several millivolts at the input to the receiver. This means that the receiver has to cope with signals over a very wide range of levels. Often signals within a few kilohertz of one another can range in strength by as much as 90dB or possibly even more. To cope with these ranges good design of the front end stages is crucial.

Under normal conditions the r.f. amplifiers should remain linear with the output remaining proportional to the input. Unfortunately even the best amplifiers have limits to their output capability, and beyond this they start to overload. When this happens their output is less than it should be, as shown in Figure 3.4. At this point the amplifier is said to be in compression.

Compression in itself is not a problem. The absolute values of a signal are of little value and in any case the a.g.c. used in most receivers means that the gain is reduced when strong signals are being received. However the side effects of compression give rise to major problems. Effects like intermodulation

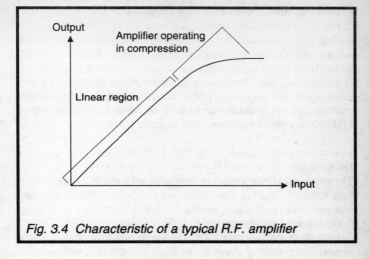

Fig. 3.4 Characteristic of a typical R.F. amplifier

distortion, cross modulation, blocking and others mean that the operation of the receiver can be seriously impaired. It is these aspects which are of great importance in the receiver design.

To help prevent these problems occurring, receivers have a number of methods of reducing the signals levels. The most important is the a.g.c. This is standard on virtually every receiver and operates on many of the amplifier stages within the set. It prevents the signals from becoming too large, especially in the later stages of the set. However it cannot always prevent the front end stages from being overloaded. This is particularly true when the offending strong signal is slightly off channel. In this case it will enter the early stages of the set but not pass through the filters. This will mean that the a.g.c. will not be affected whilst the signal is still able to overload some of the early stages. Another method of preventing overload is the use of an r.f. gain control, but like the a.g.c. this is not always effective.

Some receivers have an attenuator on the input. The level of attenuation can be increased when strong signals are on the band to prevent overloading. Often increasing the level of attenuation can enable weak signals to be heard as the effects of overloading are reduced.

One further point worthy of note is that the addition of too much gain at the front end of the receiver can cause the front end stages to overload, actually reducing the ability of the receiver to pick up and decipher weak signals. This fact should be borne in mind when adding a preamplifier to a receiver.

In view of the importance of the various aspects of overloading, a number of specifications quantify the various problems caused. However to look at these it is necessary to look at the effects and how they arise.

Distortion

The problems from compression arise as a result of the distortion which occurs to the signal when the amplifier runs into compression. The actual method which gives rise to problems may not be obvious at first sight. It can be viewed as the combination of two effects. However to see how it arises it is necessary to look at some of the basic effects of compression.

One of the forms of distortion which arises is harmonic distortion where harmonics of the wanted signal are produced. Depending upon the exact way in which the signal is compressed the levels of even order harmonics (2f, 4f, 6f, etc.) and odd order harmonics (3f, 5f, 7f, etc.) will vary. As a result of the production of these harmonics it is possible that signals below that being received could be picked up. However the r.f. tuning is likely to remove these signals before they enter the first stages of the receiver.

Another effect which can be noticed is that the amplifier tends to act as a mixer. The non-linear transfer curve means that signals will tend to mix together or modulate one another. This effect is known as intermodulation. It is unlikely that this effect on its own would give any problems. The mix products from signals close to the wanted one fall well away from the received signal. Alternatively, to produce a signal within the receiver pass-band, signals well away from the received one would need to be entering the r.f. amplifier. These would normally be rejected by the r.f. tuning. Take the example of two signals on 50.00 and 50.01MHz. These would mix together to give signals at 0.01MHz and 100.01MHz. These are not likely to give rise to any problems. This is known as a second order effect.

Problems start to arise when the two effects combine with one another. It is quite possible for a harmonic of one signal to mix with the fundamental or a harmonic of the other. The third order sum products like $2f_1 + f_2$ are unlikely to cause a problem, but the difference products like $2f_1 - f_2$ can give significant problems. Take the example of operation on the 50MHz amateur band where two strong signals are present at 50.00 and 50.01MHz. The difference signals produced will be at $2 \times 50.00 - 50.01 = 49.99$MHz and another at $2 \times 50.01 - 50 = 50.02$MHz. As it can be seen either of these could cause interference on the band. Other higher order products can also cause problems: $3f_1 - 2f_2$, $4f_1 - 3f_2$, $5f_1 - 4f_2$, and so forth, all give products which may easily be picked up. A plot of the spectrum of these odd order mix products is shown in Figure 3.5.

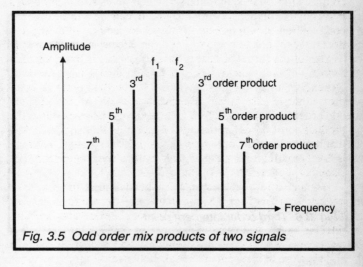

Fig. 3.5 Odd order mix products of two signals

In this way a strong signal can produce other spurious signals which can appears in its vicinity. It also means that a poor receiver may appear to pick up far more stations than a good one! The signals mixing with one another in this way may be of a variety of different types. This means that poor 3rd intermodulation performance can have the effect of raising the noise floor under real operating conditions.

Third Order Intercept

It is found that the level of intermodulation products rise very fast. For a 1dB increase in wanted signal levels, third order products will rise by 3dB, and fifth order ones by 5dB. This can be plotted to give a graph of the performance of the amplifier as shown in Figure 3.6. Eventually the amplifier will run into saturation and the levels of all the signals will be limited. However if the curve of the wanted signals and the third order products was continued, the two lines would intersect. This is known as the third order intercept point. Naturally the higher the level of the intercept point, the better the performance of the amplifier. For a good receiver an intercept point of 25dBm (i.e. 25dB above 1 milliwatt or about 0.5 watt) might be expected.

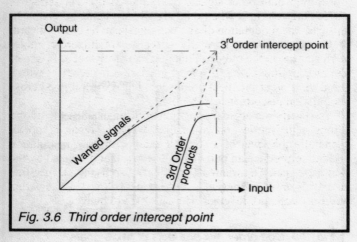

Fig. 3.6 Third order intercept point

Blocking

When a very strong off channel signal appears at the input to a receiver it is often found that the sensitivity is reduced. The effect arises because the front end amplifiers run into compression as a result of the off channel signal. This often arises when a receiver and transmitter are run from the same site and the transmitter signal is exceedingly strong. When this occurs it has the effect of suppressing all the other signals trying to pass through the amplifier, giving the effect of a reduction in gain. This can be particularly annoying when there is a strong morse signal slightly off channel. It has the effect of continually altering the gain of the receiver and varying the audio output in line with the unwanted morse signal.

Blocking is generally specified as the level of the unwanted signal at a given offset (normally 20kHz) which will give a 3dB reduction in gain. A good receiver may be able to withstand signals of about ten milliwatts before this happens.

Cross Modulation
Another effect which can be noticed when there are strong signals entering the receiver is known as cross modulation. When this occurs the modulation from a strong signal can be transferred onto other signals being picked up. This effect is particularly obvious when a.m. signals are being received. In this case the modulation of another signal can be clearly heard.

Cross modulation normally arises out of imperfect mixer performance in the radio, although it can easily occur in one of the r.f. amplifiers. As it is a third order effect, a receiver with a good third order intercept point should also exhibit good cross modulation performance.

To specify the cross modulation performance the effect of a strong a.m. carrier on a smaller wanted signal is noted. Generally the level of a strong carrier with 30% modulation needed to produce an output 20dB below that produced by the wanted signal. The wanted signal level also has to be specified and 1mV or −47dBm (i.e. a signal 47dB below 1mW) is often taken as standard, together with an offset frequency of 20kHz.

Chapter 4

SELECTIVITY

One of the major requirements of a receiver is to select the required signal and reject the unwanted ones on other frequencies. There are several ways in which unwanted signals can be allowed to pass through the receiver. The most obvious is that the basic receiver selectivity is insufficient, allowing signals on adjacent channels through. Alternatively the r.f. tuning may be insufficient, allowing the image signal through. Another problem which can arise is that a signal can break through directly into one of the i.f. stages.

Whilst all the parameters associated with selectivity have to be borne in mind when selecting or designing a receiver, the one which is most prominent is the basic selectivity of the set.

I.F. Selectivity

The basic selectivity of any superhet receiver is provided by the intermediate frequency stages. It is in these stages where stations on adjacent channels will be rejected, and the degree of selectivity here will determine the performance of the whole receiver. Any tuning provided in the r.f. amplifiers prior to the mixer are most unlikely to affect the selectivity of the set. This is used to remove problems from image responses.

If the set is a multi-conversion receiver then some selectivity will be provided in each of the stages. However the majority of the selectivity will be placed in the lowest frequency i.f. stages. Whilst each stage will provide some selectivity, in high performance receivers it will be found that a single high quality filter is used to give most of it. Being able to choose the correct item is very important and it is necessary to be able to correctly specify its performance.

Filter Operation and Specifications

Before investigating how filters are specified it is necessary to look at the characteristics of filters which are used. An ideal filter would look like that shown in Figure 4.1. The filter would be perfectly flat within the required bandwidth (the pass-band), and then the response would fall away instantly outside this (the stop-band). If this were possible then the signals would not be attenuated at all within the pass-band and they would be heard perfectly well. Outside this band in the stop-band they would be highly attenuated, and not heard. Unfortunately it is not possible to achieve a response of this nature in the real world, although filters do achieve a very remarkable degree of performance.

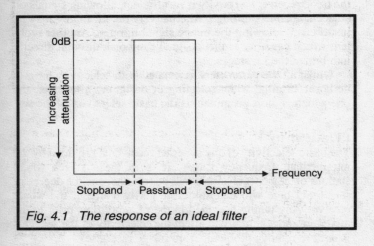

Fig. 4.1   The response of an ideal filter

As it is not possible to make an ideal filter, a response curve of a typical filter is shown in Figure 4.2, and a number of the limitations of the filters can be seen from this. In the first instance there is some loss. Normally this is around 2dB for most filters, although some very narrow band ones will have a much higher loss, possibly as much as 6 or 8dB. In either case this is not normally a problem because it can be overcome by adding additional gain within the i.f. stages to compensate.

It will also be noticed that there is a small amount of ripple on the response. This is normally one or two dB and again this is not a problem either. As a result it is not normally mentioned in receiver specifications.

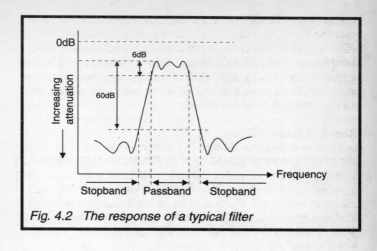

Fig. 4.2 The response of a typical filter

The more important specifications for the filter arise from the fact that the response does not fall away infinitely fast. In fact the rate of fall governs the degree to which signals on adjacent frequencies will be heard.

To specify the filter performance a number of points must be defined on the response curve. First it is necessary to determine where the pass-band lies. Normally this is taken to be within the points on the curve where the response has fallen by 6dB, i.e. where the voltage has fallen by half. As other points on the curve can be chosen the full specification for the bandwidth should also include the amount by which the response has fallen, e.g. a bandwidth of 3kHz at –6dB. If the response figure is not quoted then it is most likely to be –6dB.

Having specified the pass-band it is also necessary to specify the stop-band. Generally this is taken to be a point when the response falls to –60dB, i.e. where the voltage level is one-thousandth of the in-band level or the power is one-millionth of the in-band level.

By knowing the pass-band and the stop-band points it is possible to see how fast the filter response falls away. The "shape factor" is a measure of this, and it is often seen quoted for filters.

47

The shape factor is simply the ratio of the stop-band and pass-band values. Thus a filter having a pass-band of 6kHz at –6dB and a stop-band at –60dB outside a bandwidth of 12kHz would have a shape factor of 2:1. This is often seen quoted as a shape factor of 2:1 at 6/60dB. These figures for the attenuation should be quoted in case different points have been used for the pass-band and stop-band.

Required Bandwidths

In order to reduce the amount of interference which is received the filter bandwidth should be kept to a reasonable minimum. However as transmissions occupy a definite bandwidth, the filter must still be able to pass the whole of the transmission as shown in Figure 4.3. If a filter is too narrow then reception may be degraded because not all the signal is allowed through the filter. Typically a filter used for a.m. reception on the short wave bands will have a bandwidth of about 6kHz. On the medium wave where the top frequencies transmitted are a little higher, a wider bandwidth may be needed. For single sideband a filter bandwidth of slightly less than 3kHz is ideal. Many communications receivers will have filters which are 2.7kHz and some even as narrow as 2.1kHz. For morse, bandwidths down to 500 or even 250Hz are acceptable. The problem

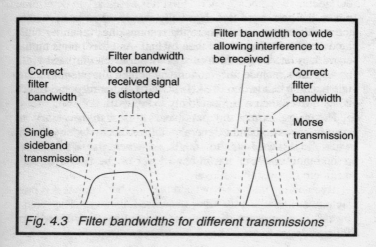

Fig. 4.3   Filter bandwidths for different transmissions

with these very narrow filters is that they make the receiver tuning more critical. It is also more difficult to locate the stations.

Types of Filter
There is a wide variety of different types of filter used within superhet radios. Some radios will simply use filters made up from the tuned transformers (L-C filters) linking the different i.f. stages within the radios. Others will also incorporate highly selective crystal filters. Each radio will have its own requirements, and the choice of filter to meet its needs without increasing the cost too much is of vital importance.

L-C Tuned Circuits
The simplest type of filter is an ordinary L-C tuned circuit. In most radios they take the form of transformers to couple the individual stage as shown in the circuit of the i.f. amplifier stage illustrated in Figure 2.8 in Chapter 2. In many receivers there will be two or three stages with tuned circuits. Using them it is usually possible to achieve sufficient selectivity for a medium wave or VHF f.m. broadcast radio. However for a good quality communications receiver it is rarely possible to be able to achieve the required degree of selectivity using just L-C filters.

If L-C filters were to be used then it would be possible to increase the degree of selectivity by increasing the number of tuned circuits between each stage. This is not ideal for a number of reasons. In the first case it increases the difficulty of aligning the set. In addition to this each tuned circuit will introduce a certain amount of loss. Increasing the number of tuned circuits will increase the amount of gain required, sometimes necessitating a further stage of gain. A further disadvantage is that it is not easy to alter the degree of selectivity by switching in additional L-C filters. If this is to be achieved then it is often preferable to switch in a further type of filter such as a crystal filter.

Crystal Filters
Crystal filters provide the main selectivity in most of today's high performance sets. They provide exceedingly high degrees

of selectivity which are hard to equal in terms of performance and cost.

The crystals in the filters are made from a substance called quartz. This is basically a form of crystalline silicon. Originally natural deposits were used to manufacture the crystals required for the electronics industry. Now quartz crystals are grown synthetically under controlled conditions to produce very high quality material.

The crystals use the piezo-electric effect for their operation. This effect occurs in a number of substances and it converts a mechanical stress into a voltage and vice versa. Many electrical transducers including microphones and the old ceramic record pick-up cartridges use it to convert sound vibrations into electrical voltages which can be amplified.

In quartz crystal resonators the piezo-electric effect is used in conjunction with the mechanical resonances which occur in the substance. The electrical signals passing into the crystal are converted into mechanical vibrations which interact with the resonances of the crystal. In this way the crystal uses the piezo-electric effect to enable the mechanical responses to tune the electrical signals. These mechanical resonances have exceedingly high Q factors. Many crystals will exhibit values of several thousand. This is many orders of magnitude higher than ordinary tuned filters made from conventional inductors and capacitors where values of a hundred or so are considered high.

Individual crystals are cut from a much larger complete crystal. The angle at which individual blanks are cut relative to the main crystal axes has a great effect on the performance of the final crystals. Mode of vibration and operation, temperature stability and many other aspects change. The cut used for most radio frequency applications is called the AT cut, although others are sometimes used.

In an electrical circuit it is often convenient to describe a particular component like a crystal in terms of simpler ones like capacitors, resistors and inductors. This makes the operation of the component much easier to see and analyze.

The equivalent circuit of a crystal is shown in Figure 4.4. In this C1 represents the capacitance between the electrodes, whilst L, C, and R represent the electrical equivalent of the

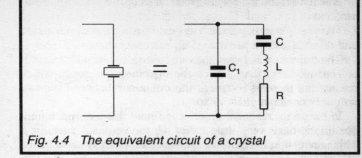

Fig. 4.4 The equivalent circuit of a crystal

mechanical or vibrational characteristics of the material. The inductance L results from the mass of the crystal, the capacitance comes from the compliance and the resistance is caused by the frictional losses in the crystal.

From the equivalent circuit it can be seen that there are two different ways in which the crystal can resonate. The first is a series resonance whose characteristics are determined by L, C, and R. In this mode the impedance seen by an external circuit is resistive and low as shown in Figure 4.5.

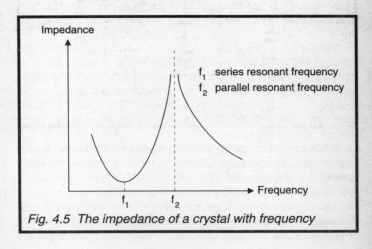

Fig. 4.5 The impedance of a crystal with frequency

51

A second resonance is also seen. This occurs when the combination of L, C, and R has an inductive reactance equivalent to C1. At this frequency the crystal exhibits a parallel resonance and offers a high impedance to an external circuit.

The difference between the two resonances is quite small. It is generally less than 1% of the operating frequency which means that in most instances the difference between the two will only be about 1kHz or so.

In the series resonant mode it is found that external circuit conditions have very little effect on the resonant frequency. This is not so in the parallel resonance mode. Any capacitance placed across the terminals will add to C1, changing the frequency of resonance. It is for this reason that crystals intended for operation in parallel resonance have a load capacitance specified. This is the value of capacitance that an external circuit must provide for the crystal to operate at its stated frequency. The most common value for crystals used by amateurs is 30pF. Crystals with a load capacitance of 20pF are also quite common, especially for higher frequencies.

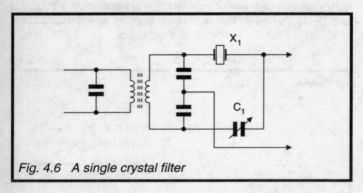

Fig. 4.6   A single crystal filter

When crystals are used in filters there is a variety of different circuit configurations which can be used. One of the most simple is a single crystal filter shown in Figure 4.6. This gives a high degree of selectivity as shown in the diagram, but has the disadvantage that the response curve is not symmetrical and has a narrow peak. This may be quite suitable for morse reception, but for modes like s.s.b. which occupy a wider bandwidth it is not ideal. In addition to this a phasing control (C1) is needed to adjust the filter for the required response.

To produce a response which is more symmetrical, a circuit using two crystals can be used. A circuit called the half-lattice filter, shown in Figure 4.7 is very widely used. This has a response that is far more even. However, within the pass-band of the filter there is a small amount of ripple. Normally the crystals will be designed to have slightly different resonant frequencies. This will mean that the filter will have a small peak at either side of the centre frequency and a small dip in the middle. As a rough rule of thumb it is found that the 3dB bandwidth of the filter is about 1.5 times the frequency difference between the two resonant frequencies. It is also found that for optimum performance the matching of the filter is very important. To achieve this, matching resistors are often placed on the input and output. If the filter is not properly matched then it is found that there will be more in-band ripple and the ultimate rejection may not be as good.

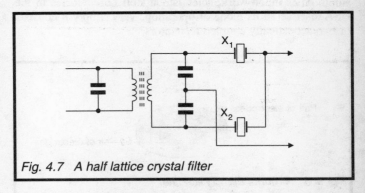

Fig. 4.7   A half lattice crystal filter

A two pole filter (i.e. one with two crystals) like that shown is not normally adequate to meet many requirements. The shape factor can be greatly improved by adding further sections. Typically ultimate rejections of 70dB and more are required in a receiver. As a rough guide a two pole filter will generally give a rejection of around 20dB; a four pole filter, 50dB; a six pole filter, 70dB; and an eight pole one, 90dB.

Monolithic Filters

With more items being integrated onto single chips these days it is hardly surprising to find that a similar approach is being adopted for crystal filters. Instead of having several separate or discrete crystals in a filter, even if they are all contained in the same can, it is possible to put a complete filter onto a single quartz crystal, hence the name monolithic crystal filter.

In essence the filter is made up by placing two sets of electrodes at opposite sides of a single AT cut crystal. The coupling between the two electrodes acts in such a way that a highly selective filter is produced.

Monolithic filters have only been available for about 25 years. Even now a large number of filter manufacturers do not produce them, preferring to use the more traditional filters made from individual crystals.

Whilst it had been known for a long while that a two pole filter could be made up on a single crystal, the idea was not developed because the way in which it worked was not understood. After much work, scientists at Bell Laboratories in the USA discovered its mode of operation. Very simply it consists of two acoustically coupled resonators.

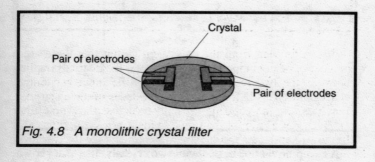

Fig. 4.8 A monolithic crystal filter

A diagram of a monolithic filter is shown in Figure 4.8. When the electrical signal is placed across one pair of electrodes, the piezo-electric effect converts this into mechanical vibrations. These travel across the crystal to the other electrodes where they are converted back into an electrical signal again. However if the acoustic signal is to travel across the crystal then its frequency must match the resonance of the crystal.

To explain the operation of the filter in terms of its electrical properties an equivalent circuit can be drawn as shown in Figure 4.9. Here L_a and C_a determine the resonant frequency of the filter. However it can be seen that there are two sections each containing these elements. As the values of these elements are set by the dimensions of the crystal, very careful control is needed to ensure that the filter functions correctly. Normally the two sections have very slightly different resonant frequencies to enable the correct bandwidth to be achieved.

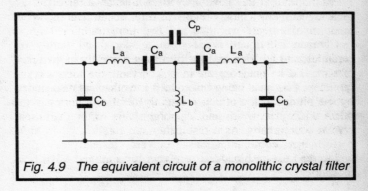

Fig. 4.9   The equivalent circuit of a monolithic crystal filter

It can be seen from the equivalent circuit that there are a number of other components present. L_b is the internal coupling between the two resonators. C_b forms the input and output capacitance. This is formed by the two faces of the electrodes. Finally, C_p is the parasitic capacitance across the whole filter and provides a path for the signal to jump across the filter. This has to be kept to an absolute minimum otherwise the filter will not reject any out of band signals sufficiently.

Normally these filters are manufactured for operation below about 30MHz, although with manufacturing techniques improving all the time it is possible to use them above this. If this is required then the normal way of accomplishing this is to use an overtone mode. This considerably increases the maximum possible frequencies, although the performance is not usually as good.

Monolithic filters are used in many areas now. They offer better performance than their discrete counterparts and they can be made smaller – a feature which is becoming increasingly important in today's miniaturised electronics industry. The main drawback of these filters is that they require very specialised equipment for their manufacture.

Ceramic Filters

Quartz is not the only substance to exhibit the piezo-electric effect combined with a sharp resonance. A number of ceramics are also used successfully to perform this function. Although filters made from these ceramics are not nearly as selective as their higher quality quartz relatives, they are cheaper and offer great improvements over their L-C counterparts.

Ceramic filters are made from a specialised family of ceramics, and the elements for filters are normally in the form of a small disc. They operate in exactly the same way as crystal filters, the signal being linked to the mechanical resonances by the piezo-electric effect. Generally ceramic filters have a much wider bandwidth and a poorer shape factor than their crystal counterparts. As a result they are rarely used in high performance communications receivers. Instead they find widespread use in broadcast receivers for a.m. and VHF f.m. reception.

Mechanical Filters

When high performance filters are needed there is another type which can be considered. Although not nearly as popular as crystal filters these days, mechanical filters found widespread use a number of years ago.

In essence their operation is very similar to that of a crystal, although the various functions are performed by individual components within the filter. At either end of the filter assembly there are transducers which convert the signals from their electrical form to mechanical vibrations, and back again at the other end. These vibrations are applied to a series of discs which are mechanically resonant at the required frequency. Each of these discs has a Q of which can be about 5000 or more, and they are arranged close to one another but not touching to form a long cylinder. A number of coupling rods are attached to run along the side of the assembly to transfer the vibrations from one section to the next. By altering the amount of coupling between the sections and the resonance of each disc, the response of the overall unit can be tailored to meet the exact requirements.

Operation of these mechanical filters is normally confined to frequencies between about 50 and 500kHz. Below these frequencies the discs become too large, whilst at the top end of the range they are too small to manufacture and mount in the filters with any degree of reliability. Apart from the limited frequency range the other disadvantage is that the resonant frequency of these filters drifts with temperature. However one of their main advantages is that exceedingly narrow bandwidths can be achieved relatively easily.

Roofing Filters
In many receivers the main filtering occurs only after there have been many stages of amplification. This means that a strong signal which is outside the pass-band of the filter like that in Figure 4.10 can cause overloading especially in the i.f. stages before the filter. This occurs because the a.g.c. will not see the signal and reduce the gain of the earlier stages to take account of it, or the operator may not be aware of the signal and reduce the r.f. gain.

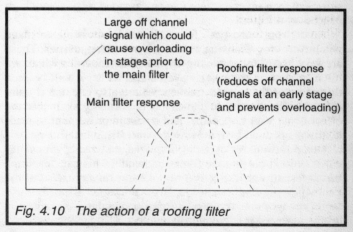

Fig. 4.10   The action of a roofing filter

57

To over come this problem a wider bandwidth filter is placed early on in the i.f. stages to reduce the level of any strong off channel signals. The main filtering, however, is still provided late on in the receiver by the main full specification filter.

These wider bandwidth "roofing" filters are often found in multi-conversion superhet receivers where the main filter is found after two or possibly three conversion stages. The roofing filter can be placed soon after the first mixer to reduce the effects of any strong off-channel signals.

Audio Filters

Very high quality filters for the i.f. stages can be very expensive. When a good filter is present and a further narrower filter is needed it can be considerably cheaper to use an audio filter. With the variety of operational amplifiers available today it is relatively easy to make good narrow band audio filters at a relatively low cost.

It is possible to design a variety of audio filters. The simpler high and low pass filters are not widely used in superhets. Instead narrow band-pass filters are often used to supplement the normal i.f. filters. Figure 4.11 shows a typical band-pass filter circuit. By choosing suitable component values the bandwidth and the centre frequency can be chosen to meet almost any requirements. If the performance of a single stage is not sufficient then several stages can be cascaded to give very high degrees of rejection.

Apart from band-pass filters, it is also possible to make notch filters for removing a narrow band of frequencies. These are very useful for removing unwanted heterodynes which are often present on the short wave bands. Whilst it will be seen that some of the wanted frequencies are also rejected (Figure 4.12), the bandwidth of the notch is normally such that the effect is not very noticeable, and a vast improvement in readability is obtained by removing the interfering heterodyne.

One disadvantage of audio filters occurs when a strong signal is present outside the filter bandwidth. This can "capture" the a.g.c. and vary the sensitivity of the receiver instead of the one which is being monitored. If the unwanted signal is varying in strength as in the case of a morse signal it can make copy of the wanted signal quite difficult.

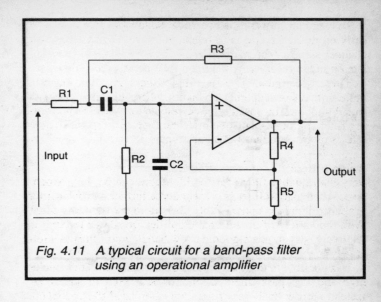

Fig. 4.11 *A typical circuit for a band-pass filter using an operational amplifier*

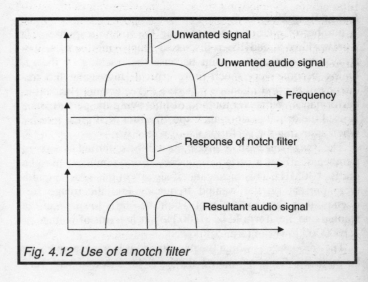

Fig. 4.12 *Use of a notch filter*

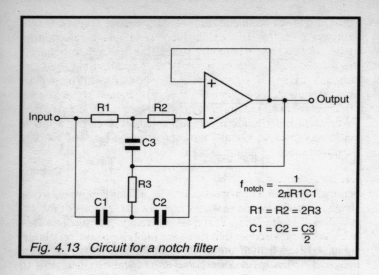

Fig. 4.13 Circuit for a notch filter

$$f_{notch} = \frac{1}{2\pi R1 C1}$$

$$R1 = R2 = 2R3$$

$$C1 = C2 = \frac{C3}{2}$$

Image Response

A number of methods of improving the image response of a receiver have already been discussed. Improving the r.f. selectivity only works to a point because the tracking of the r.f. tuning become very much more critical. Increasing the frequency of the first i.f. stage will give a greater improvement in performance. Whatever method of improving the performance is used the actual performance specification is of great interest when assessing the performance of a receiver.

The image rejection of a receiver will be specified as a given number of dB at a certain frequency. For example it may be 60dB at 30MHz. This means that if signals of the same strength were present on the wanted frequency and the image frequency, then the image signal would be 60dB lower than the wanted one, i.e. it would be 1/1000 lower in terms of voltage or 1/1000000 lower in terms of power.

The frequency at which the measurement is made also has to be included. This is because the level of rejection will vary according to the frequency in use. Many older single conversion sets with low i.f.s exhibit very poor image rejection at higher frequencies where the percentage difference between the wanted and image frequencies was small. Often they are only able to give figures of 30dB rejection or less. This would mean that at higher frequencies the weak wanted signals could often be masked out by strong signals on a different band. Fortunately most modern sets are capable of giving a much better performance. Usually they can give rejections of 80dB at most frequencies, falling to 60dB at worst.

I.F. Breakthrough

Another problem which can occur with a superhet occurs when signals from the aerial break through the r.f. sections of the set and directly enter the i.f. stages. Normally intermediate frequencies are chosen so that there are likely to be no very large signals present which might cause problems. However when the receiver has a fixed frequency first local oscillator this is not easy to ensure. The example of the amateur band receiver which has a first i.f. spanning 5.0 to 5.5MHz will cover one broadcast band where there are likely to be several high powered broadcast stations. To ensure that direct breakthrough is not a problem the circuit and the internal layout of the receiver must ensure that sufficient isolation can be achieved. Some receivers even include a filter in the r.f. stages to remove any signals which might break through.

The specification for breakthrough is quoted in the same fashion as image rejection. Normally it is possible to achieve figures of 60 to 80dB rejection, and on some receivers figures of 100dB have been quoted.

Spurious Signals

It is virtually impossible to design a radio receiver which is free from the reception of spurious signals. Often they will not be noticed when the receiver is connected to an aerial, because the incoming signals will mask them out. However when the receiver input is terminated with a matched load, it is often possible to hear a number of these unwanted signals.

These signals can arise in a number of ways. For example receivers which include a number of oscillators are likely to generate spurious signals at some frequency. Local oscillators used for frequency conversions, as well as oscillators used for microprocessor clocks are common sources. Whilst it is usually possible to reduce these signals to a level where they are not normally noticeable, it can be very difficult to eliminate them all together.

Another problem arises from the mixers which are used. Although a perfect mixer would only produce the sum and difference products, real mixers produce a number of other products. Harmonics of one of the input signals can mix with the fundamental or harmonics of the other (i.e. $mf_1 \pm mf_2$). In this way a whole variety of signals can be generated. Often receivers will use manufactured mixers bought in from mixer manufacturers. Normally the levels of unwanted mix products are reasonably well known for particular types of mixer. Often they will be at very low levels (–60dB or lower than the wanted mix products in a good mixer). With a knowledge of the unwanted frequencies which can be produced, the receiver designers can choose the basic outline of the set to avoid any significant levels of unwanted signals.

Chapter 5

LOCAL OSCILLATOR

Every superhet radio will have one or more local oscillators, one for each conversion. The performance of these oscillators governs a number of very important aspects of the receiver's operation. As a result the design of the oscillator requires very careful consideration to ensure the performance of the remainder of the radio is not impaired by this one element.

Requirements

The first requirement of the oscillator is that it should be able to tune over a sufficient range to give the receiver its complete frequency coverage. This may appear to be very obvious, but designing an oscillator to perform this function reliably is not always as easy as it sounds. This is particularly true at very high frequencies where small amounts of stray capacitance or inductance can introduce unwanted effects.

One of the most serious can be spurious oscillations. When they occur, spurious oscillations can be an annoying problem because they will enable additional signals to enter the i.f. stages, particularly if they are near to the wanted signal and they are not attenuated by the r.f. tuning.

Another major requirement of the local oscillator is that it should be stable. Any drift in its frequency will reflect in a corresponding change in the frequency to which the receiver is tuned. A certain amount of drift may be acceptable for broadcast wide-band f.m., narrow-band f.m. or a.m. signals. However even small amounts of drift will be most annoying when listening to s.s.b. or morse because it will mean that the receiver has to be re-tuned every few minutes.

Basic Oscillator

There is a wide variety of different types of circuit which can be used as an oscillator. However they all use the same basic concepts, consisting of an amplifier in which a proportion of the output is fed back to the input. The phase of this feedback is in such a sense that it reinforces the signal at the input,

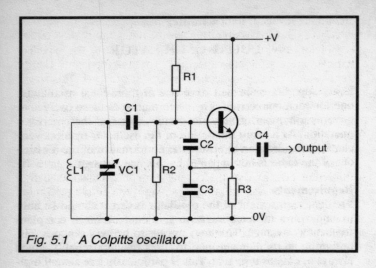

Fig. 5.1   A Colpitts oscillator

causing the circuit to break into oscillation. As the feedback reinforces the signal at the input it is called positive feedback.

Whilst there is a variety of different circuits which can be used, the one which is most commonly used is called the Colpitts oscillator. It has a number of advantages, including being a reliable and stable circuit. The fact that one side of the tuned circuit is connected to ground is also a major advantage because it means that drift caused by hand capacity and other stray effects can be reduced to a minimum. Its circuit is shown in Figure 5.1.

Oscillator Stability
To ensure that the oscillator remains stable there are a number of points which can be observed in the design of the circuit as well as in its construction.

Heat is a major cause of drift. Even small changes in temperature cause the components to expand or contract by a small amount. This is sufficient to make the resonant frequency of the circuit change. To overcome this the circuit should be kept away from any sources of heat in the equipment. Adequate ventilation should also be provided to ensure that the whole equipment, and in particular the oscillator does not experience any undue levels of temperature rise.

As it is never possible to keep the temperature of a circuit completely stable, part of the design will be to use negative temperature coefficient capacitors. These components change their value in the opposite direction to the others. In this way it is possible to balance the two effects and arrive at a circuit with the minimum amount of drift. Determining the exact values of the components to achieve this is a rewarding exercise, even though it can be very time-consuming.

Other measures to improve stability include the use of a high Q tuned circuit. This will ensure that any changes have the minimum effect. Also the circuit should be constructed in a rigid fashion as this will reduce any movement to a minimum. Particular attention should be paid to the coil. If the windings use thin wire the coil and former should be given a coat of varnish to ensure that they are held firmly in place. The quality of the tuning capacitor is also very important. It should be a high quality type with ball bearings to ensure smooth running and freedom from frequency jumps as it is tuned.

Another problem which can cause drift or frequency change is an alteration in the load impedance of the circuit. To prevent this happening, the output from the oscillator is normally fed into a buffer amplifier. This serves to reduce the effect of any load variations to a sufficiently small value. A source or emitter follower circuit is ideal for this (see Figure 5.2).

Oscillators will also drift when their operating voltage is changed. This occurs because the whole operating point of the circuit is changed. Bipolar transistors are particularly susceptible to these changes because any variation in the bias conditions will alter the internal capacitances in the transistor. In turn this will change the resonant frequency of the circuit. FETs and even thermionic valves are not immune from drift as a result of voltage changes. To overcome this problem, oscillators are invariably run from stabilised power sources. This will also help reduce other problems including noise and hum which might otherwise be present on the supply rails and modulate the signal. Today there is a wide variety of excellent voltage regulators on the market. Before using one it is worth checking its specification to ensure that its voltage is sufficiently stable with temperature.

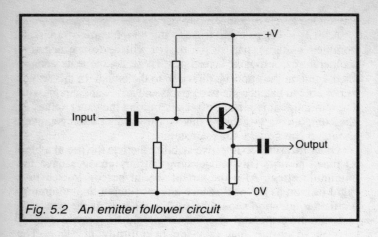

Fig. 5.2 An emitter follower circuit

Crystal Mixer Oscillator

Even a carefully designed v.f.o. will have a certain amount of drift, and this will become more pronounced at higher frequencies. At frequencies towards the top of the h.f. bands the drift can sometimes be too much for serious use. To overcome this a number of methods are available to set designers. One is to use a double conversion in the signal path, using a crystal controlled first conversion and a v.f.o. for the second as described in Chapter 2. Alternatively it is possible to have a single conversion in the signal path and mix the v.f.o. directly with a switched crystal oscillator as shown in Figure 5.3. This approach has found favour with a number of receiver designers.

In this circuit the oscillator can be run at a fairly low frequency, one commonly used for amateur receivers is 5.0 to 5.5MHz. Running at a relatively low frequency the circuit will not be subject to as much drift. In addition to this the circuit can be optimised to operate in a narrow band of frequencies. Finally the tuned circuit is not switched. This in itself is a great bonus because the use of a switch introduces longer leads and the inconsistency of the switch contacts. Both of these factors do not lend themselves to giving good stable frequency control. Instead the switch is placed in the crystal oscillator which is more able to cope with these problems, and there is considerably less effect on the overall stability.

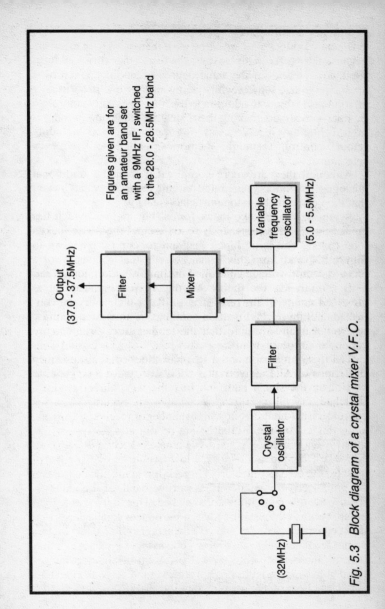

Fig. 5.3 Block diagram of a crystal mixer V.F.O.

67

Frequency Synthesizers

Frequency synthesizers are being used increasingly in receivers because they offer many advantages over other forms of local oscillator. They offer the same degree of stability given by a crystal reference source, whilst being able to tune in a virtually continuous fashion. In addition to this they are easily controlled by microprocessors making them ideal for inclusion in today's high technology receivers, offering many functions including remote control, scanning, memories, and exact frequency selection.

Although they are more complicated than the traditional analogue oscillators, integrated circuit technology has meant that they can now be made reasonably easily.

Synthesizers can take many forms, but the one which has gained universal acceptance is based around the phase locked loop (p.l.l.). The basic block diagram for a p.l.l. is shown in Figure 5.4, and from this it can be seen that it consists of a phase detector, voltage controlled oscillator (v.c.o.), loop filter, and a reference oscillator. As the frequency stability is governed totally by the reference oscillator, this is crystal controlled, and this circuit is often contained within a temperature controlled oven to ensure that the temperature variations are kept to an absolute minimum.

The operation of the basic phase locked loop is fairly straightforward. The reference oscillator and v.c.o. produce

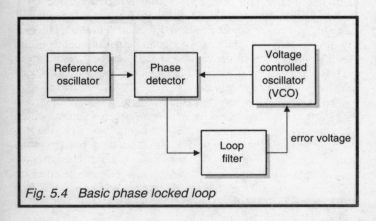

Fig. 5.4   Basic phase locked loop

signals which both enter the phase detector. This circuit produces a signal which is proportional to the phase difference between the two signals. This voltage is passed through the loop filter which is essentially a form of low pass filter which performs several functions. It controls the loop stability, controls many of the loop characteristics, and determines the level of spurious sidebands generated by the loop. Its design is crucial to the correct operation, but the choice of values in it are often a careful compromise between several different requirements.

Once through the filter the error voltage is applied to the control input of the v.c.o. In fact the sense of the error voltage is such that it reduces the phase difference between the signal from the v.c.o. and that of the reference.

When the loop is locked and in its steady state, the error voltage will be constant and proportional to the phase difference between the two signals. As the phase difference between the two signals is not changing this means that the v.c.o. is on EXACTLY the same frequency as the reference.

To use the phase locked loop as a synthesizer it is necessary to include some method of changing the output frequency to whatever is required. There are two basic methods of doing this. One entails placing a digital divider into the loop, and the other uses a mixer.

The first method of changing the output frequency is to use a digital divider. This is placed into the loop between the v.c.o. and the phase detectors shown in Figure 5.5. It has the effect of dividing the frequency of the v.c.o. by whatever ratio it is set to. In turn this has the effect of raising the output frequency of the loop in proportion to the division ratio. In other words, if the division ratio of the divider is two, then the output frequency of the loop will be raised by two.

To see how this works, take the example of the division ratio set to two. The phase detector generates an error voltage which has the effect of reducing the phase difference between the two signals entering the phase detector, making them both have the same frequency. For this to be true the v.c.o. signal must have a frequency twice that of the phase detector comparison frequency, i.e. twice the reference frequency. The same is also true for a division ratio of three, four, and so forth.

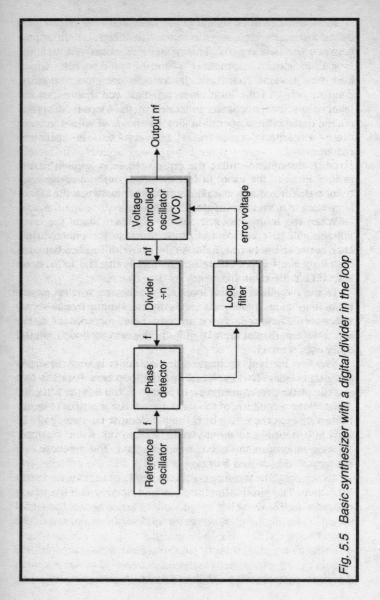

Fig. 5.5 Basic synthesizer with a digital divider in the loop

From this it will be seen that the v.c.o. can step in multiples of the reference frequency. In fact by making the divider programmable, it is very easy to change the frequency of the loop. By changing the division ratio by one, the frequency of the loop will change by an increment equal to the reference frequency. This means that for a 25kHz step, the reference frequency must be equal to 25kHz. It is not normally possible to have a crystal oscillator running at such a low frequency. Instead a divider is placed after the reference oscillator to reduce the frequency to the desired frequency (Figure 5.6). This divider will have a fixed division ratio unlike the one in the loop itself which is programmable. For example, the reference can run at a convenient frequency such as 1MHz and then a divider with a division ratio of forty can be placed after it to reduce the frequency appearing at the phase detector to 25kHz.

Using a digital divider in a phase locked loop is not the only technique which can be used when making a synthesizer. It is also possible to use a mixer as shown in Figure 5.7 to generate a frequency offset in the loop.

In view of the fact that this technique uses what is essentially an analogue technique, this type of synthesizer is sometimes called an analogue synthesizer. This is in contrast to the loop with a digital divider which is often called a digital synthesizer.

The way the loop accommodates the mixer is very similar to that when a divider is used. When the loop is in lock the two signals at the inputs to the phase detector must be exactly the same. However by tracing the signal back it is possible to determine the frequency at which the v.c.o. must be operating. To help illustrate the way in which this works some example figures have been included in the diagram. Taking these, the reference oscillator is running at 1MHz and the external frequency is 5MHz. This means that for the phase detector to see a frequency of 1MHz the v.c.o. must be running at a frequency of either 4MHz or 6MHz. As it is more usual to mix the signal down in frequency it is more likely that the v.c.o. would be operating at 6MHz.

From this it can be seen that problems might arise from the fact that two possible mix products could give the required 1MHz output. In view of the phasing in the loop, only one

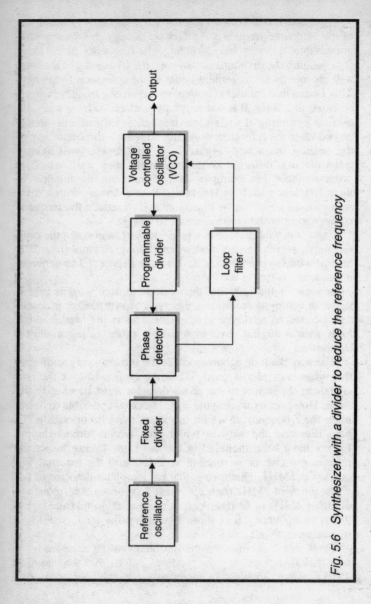

Fig. 5.6 Synthesizer with a divider to reduce the reference frequency

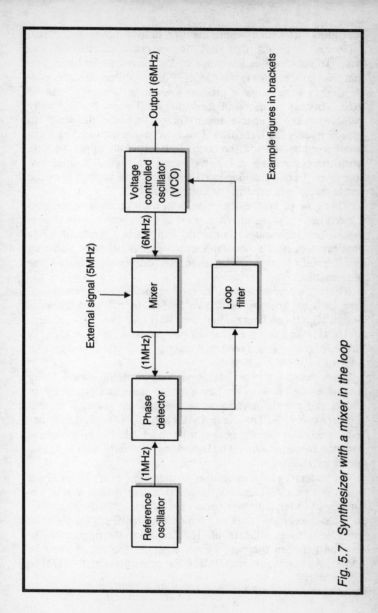

Fig. 5.7 Synthesizer with a mixer in the loop

73

condition will actually cause the loop to lock, however it is still necessary to ensure that only one of these possibilities can arise. To achieve this the range of the v.c.o. can be limited so that the v.c.o. cannot reach 4MHz. For loops that need to operate over a wide range a process known as "steering" can be used. This can be accomplished in several ways, but it usually involves using a coarse tune voltage to place the v.c.o. in approximately the right area. This is normally supplied by electronic circuits outside the loop. Possibly data might be sent from the controlling microprocessor to a digital to analogue converter. To pull the loop into lock a fine tune voltage from the phase detector is used in the normal way.

This type of synthesizer is seldom used on its own. Instead it becomes very useful when used in conjunction with digital synthesizer techniques. By placing a mixer in a synthesizer it is possible to cascade several loops together, thereby allowing much smaller steps to be used without compromising the performance.

There are several ways of designing multi-loop synthesizers. One possible method is shown in Figure 5.8, and shows a design which can operate between 10.0 and 19.9MHz in steps of 100kHz and using a division ratio of less than 20. Using a single loop this would require a maximum division ratio of 199, a factor of about ten higher.

The operation of the first loop is very straightforward, being a simple digital loop. It has a phase detector frequency of 1MHz and a division ratio between 9 and 18, giving it an output between 9 and 18MHz in 1MHz steps. The second loop has a division ratio varying between 10 and 19, but having a phase detector frequency of 100kHz making it able to step in increments of 100kHz.

To understand the operation of this loop, take the example when the first divider loop is set to 9, this means that a frequency of 9MHz will be entering the mixer. If the division ratio in the second loop is set to 10 then the frequency coming out must be 10 times 100kHz, i.e. 1MHz. In turn the frequency difference between the two signals entering the mixer must be 1MHz. As one signal is at 9MHz, the other must be 9 + 1MHz, i.e. 10MHz.

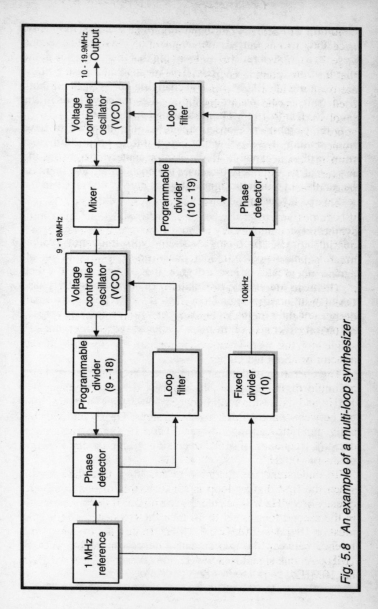

Fig. 5.8 An example of a multi-loop synthesizer

To take the other end of the tuning range, the first loop is set to 18 and gives an output into the mixer of 18MHz. The second loop has a division ratio of 19 meaning that the frequency at the output of the mixer is 1.9MHz. This means that the v.c.o. must be operating at 19.9MHz. By changing the values of both dividers it is possible to set the synthesizer anywhere in the range 10MHz to 19.9MHz in steps of 100kHz.

If the number of loops is extended it is possible to have much smaller step sizes whilst being able to keep the divider ratios within acceptable limits. Unfortunately increasing the number of loops greatly increases the cost. It can also increase the number of spurious signals if great care is not taken in the design and layout of the circuit.

Phase Noise
One of the major problems associated with frequency synthesizers is phase noise. In fact phase noise is present on all signals to a greater or lesser degree. It is basically noise which is present as frequency modulation, or more correctly phase modulation on the signal. In fact it corresponds to small amounts of jitter on the signal, and it shows up as noise spreading out on either side of the main carrier as shown in Figure 5.9.

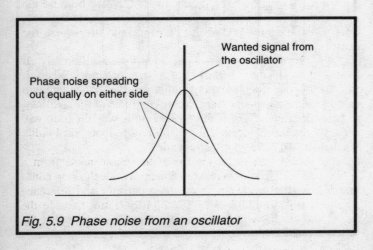

Fig. 5.9 Phase noise from an oscillator

In most cases the levels of the phase noise are relatively low. Any oscillator with a high Q element as the tuned circuit will be very good. Crystal oscillators are very good, and free running variable frequency oscillators also produce low levels of phase noise. However because of the way in which a synthesizer works, it is possible for the levels of phase noise to be much higher, especially when the division ratios are high.

The phase noise is generated within three main areas of the synthesizer loop: the v.c.o.; phase detector; and the reference oscillator. The v.c.o. is a major cause of phase noise. Being tuned electronically by varactor diodes and having a wide range it will naturally have a low Q. The phase detector and reference oscillator have a much better performance but this can be degraded by the operation of the loop. To see how this happens it is necessary to look at the loop in a little more detail.

When the loop is locked a steady state error voltage will be produced by the phase detector. This will pass through the filter and be applied to the control terminal of the v.c.o. Filtering will allow through only the low frequencies on the tune voltage. So any noise produced by the reference or phase detector will only appear at the control terminal of the v.c.o. if it is within the loop bandwidth. Whilst it may appear from first sight that any levels of noise from the phase detector and reference will be very low, this is not always the case because the level of this noise is multiplied by the division ratio in the loop. This means that the higher the division ratio, the worse the noise.

Noise generated by the v.c.o. is affected differently. It passes through the dividers and phase detector. When it reaches the loop filter, anything within the filter bandwidth will pass through and appear at the control terminal of the oscillator to counteract the effect of the noise. In this way the loop will actually attenuate v.c.o. noise within the loop bandwidth, whereas it will have no effect outside.

This means that the make up of the phase noise from a synthesizer will have several constituents. Inside the loop bandwidth it will be made up from phase detector and reference oscillator noise multiplied by the division ratio. Outside the loop bandwidth it will be from the v.c.o. This means that the

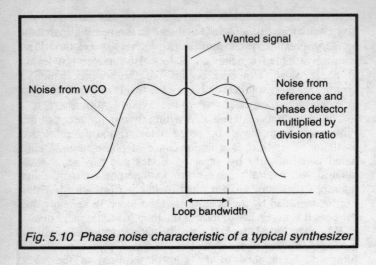

Fig. 5.10 Phase noise characteristic of a typical synthesizer

shape of the noise is likely to be similar to that shown in Figure 5.10.

Reciprocal Mixing
Often the results of phase noise on a local oscillator will go unnoticed. On a clear band with few strong signals it is unlikely that any effects will be heard. However the case is very different when weak signals are being sought in the presence of much stronger ones.

To illustrate the effect of reciprocal mixing take the case when a strong signal is being received. Here the local oscillator will be mixed with the incoming signal to generate the mix product at the intermediate frequency of the receiver. In this way the incoming signal will pass through the filters and will be heard. However as the receiver is tuned off the strong signal it would normally fall outside the pass-band of the filters and remain undetected. If the receiver local oscillator has a high level of phase noise then this phase noise can mix with the off channel station to produce a noise product which falls within the receiver pass-band. This noise can mask out the weaker stations on the band which are being sought. The level of phase noise generally falls as the frequency offset from the local oscillator increases. This means that the further the strong signal is away from the frequency being received the lower the noise level from the reciprocal mixing effect is (Figure 5.11).

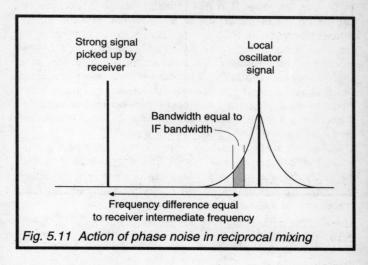

Fig. 5.11 Action of phase noise in reciprocal mixing

Stability Specifications

The stability of a receiver is of great importance. Today most high quality sets use a frequency synthesizer, and as a result drift can be reduced to very low levels. For receivers with free running variable frequency oscillators, drift can be more of a problem.

When specifying drift manufacturers normally quote the amount of drift in a given time, normally an hour. Typically a specification may give a figure of 100Hz per hour. This is specified after a given warm up time. For valve sets this is often an hour, whereas semiconductor sets will settle more quickly and the drift is often quoted after a warm up time of half an hour.

The specifications for crystals and crystal oscillators are quoted in a slightly different way. For a crystal any accuracy figures are likely to be quoted in p.p.m. This stands for a number of parts per million tolerance. If a crystal has an accuracy of 1 p.p.m., and its operating frequency is 10MHz, then its tolerance or error would be 10Hz.

A number of different accuracy figures are quoted. First is the initial tolerance. This is the accuracy to which the crystal is manufactured. Secondly its drift with temperature. This is normally over the range 0 to 70˚C. Finally there is a specification for the ageing of the crystal. It is found that crystals change their frequency with time as a result of imperfections entering the outer parts of the crystal lattice and changing the resonant frequency very slightly. To reduce this crystals are now enclosed in a hermetically sealed can which is either evacuated or filled with an inert gas. Even so some ageing occurs, and this figure is often quoted as a number of parts per million per year. Although a crystal ages fastest during its first months of operation a worst case figure must be quoted.

All of this means that there is no single figure which can be quoted for a crystal. At any time its frequency of operation will be within the total tolerance which can be calculated by adding the initial tolerance, temperature stability and the ageing rate, calculated for the individual case in question.

Crystal ovens have similar specifications. Their tolerances are rarely quoted in p.p.m. Their accuracy is usually at least an order of magnitude better than that of a straight crystal and often two orders of magnitude better. In view of this their tolerances are normally quoted as parts in 10^n. In other words a tolerance of 1 in 10^7 would given an error of 1Hz on a 10MHz oscillator.

The figures for ovens normally include ageing, operating over a temperature range, and the effect of load and supply voltage changes. Again there is not a simple figure for the tolerance of the signal which will be produced. However a crystal oven will normally be able to produce a reference signal which is more than accurate enough for most UHF, VHF and HF applications.

Chapter 6

DEMODULATION

One of the key stages in any radio is the demodulator. Here the information or modulation from the radio signal is removed from the carrier and converted to a baseband signal. In most cases this means generating the audio signal which can be amplified by an audio amplifier before being passed into the loudspeaker or a pair of headphones.

There is a wide variety of different types of modulation which can be picked up on the airwaves. A.m., narrow and wide-band f.m., s.s.b., morse, and of course there are many more, including various forms of data transmission. To be able to resolve any of these types of modulation, the correct demodulator must be used. If the wrong type of demodulator is used then it is quite possible that the resulting audio will be totally indecipherable, or even non-existent.

A.M. Detector

The simplest type of detector is the diode detector used for a.m. A circuit of a simple diode detector is shown in Figure 6.1 and it operates by detecting the envelope of the incoming signal. It achieves this by simply rectifying the signal. Current is allowed to flow through the diode in only one direction, giving either the positive or negative half of the envelope at the output. If the detector is to be used only for detection it does not matter which half of the envelope is used, either will work equally well. Only when the detector is also used to supply the a.g.c. circuitry will the polarity of the diode matter.

The detector will normally include a small capacitor at the output to remove any r.f. components of the signal at the output. The value is chosen so that it does not affect the audio base-band signal. The individual circuits to which the a.g.c. voltage is applied will normally have additional filtering or smoothing to remove any inter-stage coupling which could lead to instability. This filtering will also remove any of the modulation present on the a.g.c. line so that only a d.c. voltage is applied to the previous stages to control their gain.

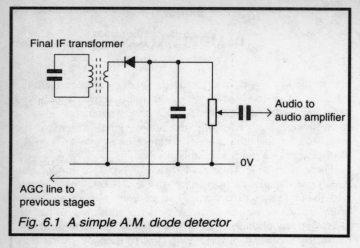

Final IF transformer

AGC line to
previous stages

Audio to
audio amplifier

0V

Fig. 6.1 A simple A.M. diode detector

This type of detector is called a linear envelope detector because the output is proportional to the input envelope. Unfortunately the diodes used can introduce appreciable levels of harmonic distortion unless modulation levels are kept low. To overcome these and other problems, synchronous detectors can be used. However before explaining the operation of these detectors it is first necessary to outline the methods of detecting s.s.b. and morse signals.

Morse and S.S.B. Detection

A.m. is only used for limited applications these days. For long distance communications on the high frequency bands single sideband and morse are far more efficient. However to be able to copy these modes a more complicated detector circuit is needed.

A morse signal usually consists of a carrier being turned on and off to create the dots and dashes. With a simple diode detector these would appear in the loudspeaker as a series of clicks or thumps which would be very difficult to decipher. If the incoming signal is to be copied it must be converted into an audio tone. This is easily achieved by beating the signal with an internal oscillator placed slightly off frequency. The two signals are mixed in a mixer in exactly the same way as the frequency

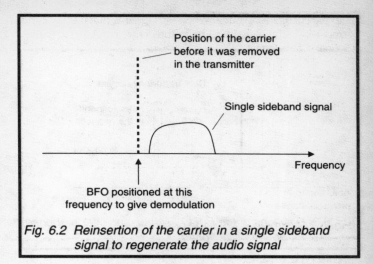

Fig. 6.2 *Reinsertion of the carrier in a single sideband signal to regenerate the audio signal*

conversion earlier in the set. The difference in frequency between the incoming signal and the internal oscillator is equal in frequency to the audio tone which is generated.

The same circuitry is also used to resolve single sideband signals. The single sideband signal consists of one sideband and no carrier. This carrier has to be reinserted at the correct frequency as shown in Figure 6.2.

Although the mixer used in this process performs exactly the same function as any other mixer, it is often called a product detector. This name is derived from the fact that its output is the product of the two inputs. The local oscillator is generally called a beat frequency oscillator (b.f.o.), although in some instances it may be known as a carrier insertion oscillator (c.i.o.).

To obtain the optimum results when operating the receiver, the signal is tuned to the centre of the receiver pass-band. The beat frequency oscillator is adjusted so that it occurs on the same frequency relative to the s.s.b. signal as the carrier would have been, as shown in Figure 6.3. For morse reception a similar approach is adopted. The signal is tuned to the centre of the pass-band and the b.f.o. is positioned to give the correct pitch notes. In normal operation the position of the b.f.o. is preset to the correct frequency. When the signal is tuned to give the correct pitch, the signal will be in the centre of the pass-band.

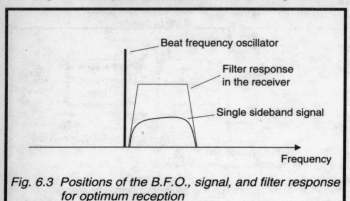

Fig. 6.3 Positions of the B.F.O., signal, and filter response for optimum reception

Synchronous A.M. Detection

Ordinary envelope detection for a.m. has several disadvantages. Many of these are overcome by using a form of detection known as synchronous detection. This operates using what is essentially a beat frequency oscillator and mixer in very much the same way as in the detection of s.s.b. and morse. To ensure that the beat frequency oscillator is on exactly the correct frequency it is synchronised to the incoming carrier frequency.

Synchronisation of the carrier can be achieved in a number of ways. A narrow band filter can be used to extract the carrier and then this can be mixed with the incoming signal. This is the most obvious method, but it has the drawback that the carrier has to be positioned on exactly the correct frequency for it to operate correctly. Alternatively a phase locked loop can be used. The loop will lock onto the incoming carrier and generate a signal which can be fed into the mixer. A third method feeds the incoming signal into a very high gain amplifier. If the gain is sufficiently high then circuit will limit, removing the modulation and leaving only the carrier. This is then mixed with the original signal to regenerate the original audio. This last method is the cheapest and it does not have the limitations of a very limited band of operation of the filter method. A low pass filter is incorporated after the mixer. This removes any of the high frequency mix products. A simple R-C network usually suffices.

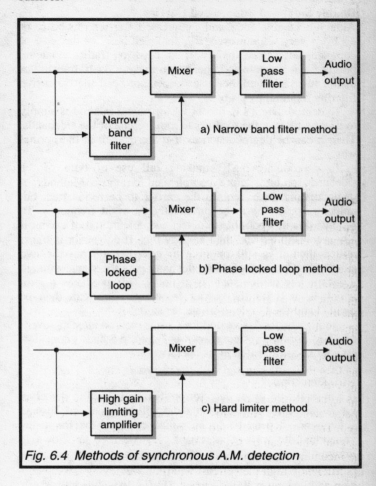

Fig. 6.4 Methods of synchronous A.M. detection

Using a synchronous detector much lower levels of distortion can be achieved. In addition to this the effects of selective fading which are often encountered on the short wave bands can be minimised. As a result this form of detection is used in many high grade communications receivers.

Double Sideband Suppressed Carrier

Although Double Sideband Suppressed Carrier (d.s.b.s.c. or d.s.b.) is very seldom used, it is included here for the sake of completeness. Occasionally it is used by radio amateurs because it is simpler and cheaper to make a d.s.b. transmitter than a full s.s.b. one, because it does not need the expensive filtering required by s.s.b.

To demodulate d.s.b. the most convenient method is simply to use the filter in the receiver to remove one of the sidebands. Then it can be demodulated as if it were s.s.b. in the normal way.

To demodulate d.s.b., making full use of both of the sidebands requires more complicated circuitry. Methods of demodulating d.s.b. require the carrier to be re-inserted, but unlike s.s.b., it has to be on exactly the right frequency. To achieve this it is possible to detect a small amount of carrier if any is transmitted and then amplify this. If no carrier is transmitted then it is still possible to generate it from the two sidebands. One way of doing this is to pass the signal through a square law device such as a diode. This produces a term which is at twice the carrier frequency. This can then be divided and used to demodulate the signal.

Another method is named the Costas method after its inventor. This uses the system shown in Figure 6.5 and is considerably more complicated in its operation.

F.M. Detection

If a normal a.m. diode detector on its own is used to detect an f.m. signal, it is likely that no audio will be generated. Instead a frequency dependent circuit which converts the frequency variations into voltage variations must be used as shown in Figure 6.6.

It can be seen from the diagram that as the frequency increases, so does the voltage from the detector, and as the frequency falls so does the voltage. Normally the phase of the output is not a problem. It is just as valid for the detector output to fall as the frequency increases, again the output from the

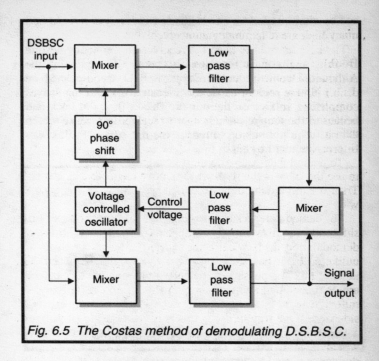

Fig. 6.5 The Costas method of demodulating D.S.B.S.C.

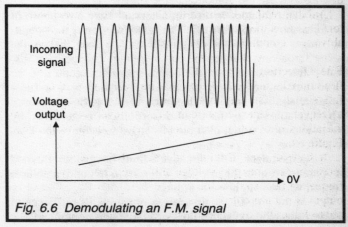

Fig. 6.6 Demodulating an F.M. signal

detector may be used for an automatic frequency control (a.f.c.) found on some older analogue receivers.

The a.f.c. is used to keep the receiver on frequency despite any drift in the local oscillator. It operates by removing the modulation from the audio output. This is accomplished by using a simple resistor capacitor filter network and this leaves a d.c. offset voltage on the output. This is then fed back and applied to the local oscillator of the receiver in a sense which will pull it in a direction to reduce the d.c. offset. In this way the receiver will be kept in tune.

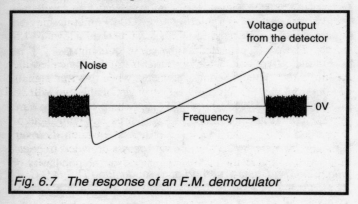

Fig. 6.7 The response of an F.M. demodulator

F.m. demodulators or discriminators all have a response of the form shown in Figure 6.7. The centre section is the operating range, and from the diagram it can be seen that as the carrier frequency changes the output voltage changes. For distortion free demodulation the centre operating section of the curve must be completely linear. Any deviation from a linear characteristic will result in distortion of the audio waveform. Whilst relatively high levels of distortion can be tolerated by communications users, hi-fi circuits strive to achieve the lowest distortion levels possible.

The demodulator will only have a finite bandwidth. Beyond its operating region the response will start to fall until a point is reached where only noise is present.

One of the significant advantages of f.m. is its resilience to interference. With no signal present a large noise output will be present. As a frequency modulated signal is introduced into the detector the noise level decreases sharply, and almost disappears for a sufficiently strong signal. In fact the noise level will be much lower than for a similar strength amplitude modulated signal.

This effect is known as quieting and a sensitivity specification is associated with this effect. When no signal is present a certain level of audio noise will be present. When a signal is introduced the noise level will fall. The quieting is the ratio of the two noise levels. Often a receiver sensitivity will be quoted for a given quieting level. For a narrow band f.m. receiver a typical sensitivity of 0.5 microvolts for 20dB quieting may be expected. For a wide band f.m. broadcast receiver a level of 1.5 microvolts may be expected to give 30dB quieting.

Another effect associated with the use of f.m. is called the capture effect. This phenomenon occurs when two f.m. signals are being picked up and only the stronger of the two will be audible at the receiver output. This is in sharp contrast to a.m. systems where the unwanted signal causes annoying heterodynes and background interference dependent upon its level. The capture effect is very useful on today's crowded frequencies and it is one of the major advantages for the popularity of f.m. in mobile v.h.f. and u.h.f. applications.

The capture effect is often quoted as a figure when it is called the capture ratio. This is defined as the ratio between the wanted and unwanted signals to give a specified reduction in the unwanted signal. Normally a ratio of 30dB for the wanted to unwanted signal is used for this. Typically one might expect to see a capture ratio of 2dB for a typical broadcast tuner. This means that if the wanted signal is 2dB stronger than the unwanted one then it will capture the demodulator and suppress the unwanted signal by 30dB.

There are a number of different circuits which can be used to demodulate f.m. The first point which will be noticed about them all is that they are more complicated than the basic single diode a.m. detector. At the very least two diodes are needed with other circuitry as well. However as f.m. is used to carry the high fidelity V.H.F. f.m. transmissions many would argue the added expense and complexity is well worthwhile.

Two of the more common circuits are called the ratio

detector, and the other is called the Foster-Seeley detector after its inventors. Phase locked loops are also widely used as well. All of them perform well, and these days most of the circuits can be obtained within integrated circuits.

F.M. Ratio Detector

The radio detector is shown in Figure 6.8. In the circuit the diodes are in series. This means that when a carrier is applied to the circuit, a steady voltage appears across the resistors R1 and R2. As a result C1 is charged up.

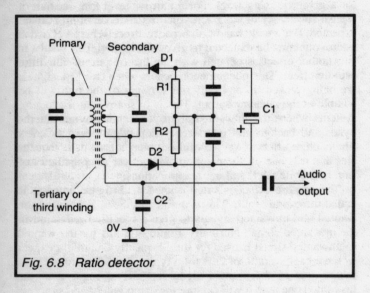

Fig. 6.8 Ratio detector

In the i.f. transformer at the heart of the ratio detector there is a third winding which is connected to the centre tap of the secondary. The basis of the operation of the circuit lies in the phasing of the signals in the circuit. The transformer is designed so that the coupling between the primary and the third winding, which is untuned, is very tight. This results in the phase of the signals in both windings being the same.

The same is not true for the primary and secondary. It is found that when the primary and secondary windings of a transformer are tuned to the same frequency, the signals at the input and output of the transformer will be different by 90°. Consequently the signal in the secondary varies from the primary by this amount.

It is found that when the signal is frequency modulated the phase of the signal in the secondary moves in comparison to the primary. This occurs as the signal moves away from the resonant frequency of the transformer.

This means that the phase difference between the third winding and the secondary change. This results in the signal from the third winding subtracting from the signal across one half of the secondary and adding to the other half. In turn this causes an imbalance to appear across the resistors R1 and R2, and hence a current flows through the third winding. This results in the audio modulation appearing at the output of the third winding.

Foster-Seeley Detector

The Foster-Seeley circuit is very similar in many respects to the ratio detector in its basic topology. Of the two the Foster-Seeley circuit is more commonly used. The reason for this is that the transformer used in the ratio circuit is more complicated and more costly. The choke used in the Foster-Seeley circuit is generally cheaper than the addition of the third winding to the transformer.

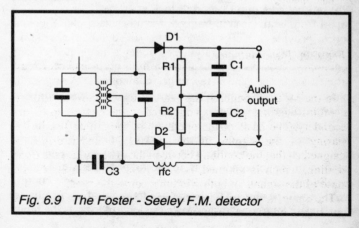

Fig. 6.9   The Foster - Seeley F.M. detector

This circuit has a number of differences when compared to the ratio detector. However its method of operation bears many similarities, and depends upon the relative phases of the signals at the input and output of a tuned transformer for its operation.

In this circuit a connection is made from the primary circuit to the secondary circuits using a capacitor C3. This is connected from the signal side of the primary (e.g. the collector of the driving transistor) to the centre tap of the secondary winding. This gives a signal which is 90° out of phase.

In the steady state when a carrier is present at the centre of the band, both diodes D1 and D2 will conduct, producing equal but opposite voltages across their load resistors R1 and R2. As the audio output is the sum of the voltages across these two resistors, the resultant signal will be zero when the carrier is centred in this way.

When the carrier frequency varies from the centre the balance condition will be destroyed and one diode will conduct more than the other. This results in the voltages across R1 and R2 becoming different and a signal appearing at the output terminals.

The choke, r.f.c. is included in the circuit to prevent any of the radio frequency signal appearing at the output. Similarly the capacitors C1 and C2 placed across the resistors R1 and R2 also provide a filtering function.

Phase Locked Loop Demodulators

Apart from being used in frequency synthesizers, phase locked loops provide a very good means of demodulating f.m. Requiring no coils and relying on today's integrated circuit technology it is possible to make a high performance circuit from a single i.c. and a few other components. As a result, phase locked loop demodulators are being used increasingly in all types of radio receiver.

The method of operation is quite simple. Referring to the basic block diagram of a phase locked loop shown in Figure 5.4, the signal from the intermediate frequency stages is applied to the reference input to the loop. Under steady state conditions the loop will remain in lock and a steady control voltage will be applied to the control terminal of the oscillator to maintain its frequency and keep the loop in lock. If the input frequency varies then the oscillator will have to change its frequency for lock to be maintained. In turn this requires the control voltage to vary. In other words the control voltage varies according to the input frequency and is the demodulated f.m. This voltage is buffered and then taken outside the phase locked loop i.c. to be amplified by the audio amplifier.

Using current i.c. technology it is possible to make the voltage to frequency characteristic of the oscillator very linear. This results in linear demodulation and very low levels of distortion. Coupled to the low cost of a phase locked loop demodulator both of these factors make this type of circuit very attractive.

Chapter 7

OPERATION

Many of today's radios are very high performance pieces of equipment. They contain large amounts of circuitry and as a result they are able to support a wide variety of features on top of possessing a good basic specification. However to reach their full potential they must be operated correctly. This is not always as easy as it might seem because many radios have large numbers of controls which must be used correctly. Despite this one of the first requirements is not directly a function of the radio itself. It is the aerial.

Aerial

Although transistor portable sets for use as broadcast receivers have just their own internal ferrite rod aerials, most other sets use some other form of external aerial. Even sets for broadcast V.H.F. f.m. reception as well as many World Band receivers and scanners will have a telescopic aerial attached to the set. Many "communications receivers" have no aerial of their own, only a socket for an external aerial.

For the serious user a good external aerial is needed even if the set has its own telescopic aerial. A good aerial will enable the set to reach its full potential whereas a poor one will severely limit what the set can do. There is little point in spending a vast amount of money on the receiver, only to prevent it performing properly by using an inferior aerial.

Aerials take many forms, and different types of aerial will be needed for different types of listening. For the listener to the short wave or high frequency (H.F.) bands up to frequencies of around 30MHz an end fed wire (sometimes called a long wire) is a good compromise. It can be easily erected outside as shown in Figure 7.1, and then tuned with an aerial tuning unit (a.t.u.) to ensure it is at resonance and presents the right impedance to the set. These a.t.u.s can be bought or easily made using a variable capacitor and a tapped coil. Often aerial kits for end fed wires can be obtained from electronics or short wave radio stockists.

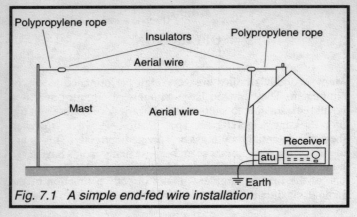

Fig. 7.1 A simple end-fed wire installation

For the scanner enthusiast a discone is probably the best all round aerial to use. These aerials are designed to cover a wide range of frequencies and they are easy to obtain from most scanner stockists.

Whatever the type of aerial in use it should be properly installed. It should be positioned as high as reasonably possible to give it the best radio "view" and it should be kept away from objects which may act as a screen. In addition it should be positioned away from any sources of interference. However for convenience, the most likely place for a discone is on a chimney. This will keep it reasonably high and the levels of interference from sources around the home should be tolerable.

Other points to watch when installing aerials is that they should be mechanically sound. Injury and damage can result if they fall down. Also great care should be taken to ensure that they cannot fall onto any live power lines. This has proved fatal in a number of instances in the past.

For anyone thinking of installing an aerial there are many books on this subject which are worth consulting to ensure that the most suitable aerial is chosen.

Receiver Controls
The operation of radios will vary from one type of receiver to the next. However as there are many common features it is

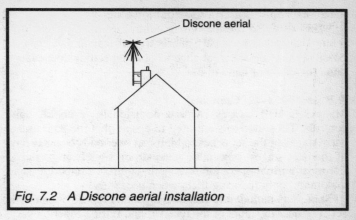

Fig. 7.2 A Discone aerial installation

possible to give an over-view of the various controls and features which can be found on many receivers today.

Tuning

The tuning control is the most used control on any set – particularly on communications receivers, it normally occupies the central position and is the largest control on the set. It should also be ergonomically placed so that it can be used with the minimum amount of strain. To achieve this the control should be placed so that the set can be tuned with the majority of the arm resting on the table surface.

The mechanics of the tuning control are important. Often weighted knobs or flywheels are used to give the right feel to the tuning. However, one important factor is that there should be no backlash on the system. If there is any backlash on the tuning it can cause considerable annoyance to the operator because when wanting to change the direction of tuning, the backlash has to be taken up before the frequency changes. This is very important when making small adjustments to the frequency, especially when tuning in s.s.b. or morse signals when minor adjustments are often needed.

In many sets these days it is possible to change the rate of tune. This feature can be very useful as large rates of tune are needed when scanning over large bands or for tuning in modes like wide-band f.m., whereas slow rates of tune are needed to make fine adjustments on s.s.b. or morse signals.

Many sets also use the tuning control to tune between different channels. This is particularly true of scanners where it is possible to set up different channel spacing settings dependent upon the mode or band in use.

R.F. and I.F. Gain Controls

Many sets will include r.f. and occasionally even i.f. gain controls. These controls are used to ensure that the gain in the early stages of the set is not so high that overloads occur in any of the later stages, especially when strong signals are present. For most normal operation these gain controls can be left near maximum, only reducing them when necessary.

Some sets include r.f. attenuators instead. These attenuators act at or near the input of the receiver and fulfil a function very similar to the r.f. gain control. The attenuation can be increased to reduce the signal levels when strong signals are present.

Mode Switch

There is a very wide variety of different modes of transmission which can be pick up. To be able to resolve them a variety of different demodulators are needed, and this necessitates a switch to enable the correct one to be used.

Sets for use on the H.F. bands will normally be able to resolve a.m., s.s.b., and morse. In fact there will often be positions for upper and lower sideband as the b.f.o. position has to be adjusted differently. Occasionally there may be a position for narrow-band f.m. (n.b.f.m.).

In view of the different modes encountered on frequencies above 30MHz, scanners will need to resolve other modes. They will normally be able to resolve a.m., narrow-band f.m. and wide-band f.m. Sets which can cover the short wave bands may also have positions for s.s.b. and morse. On some scanners the mode switch is automatically determined by the frequency in use. Normally it is only possible to find one particular mode on any given band. It is possible to link the mode selection to the frequency. However this is not always true and the more experienced user will want to have the freedom to select the required mode.

Filter Selection

As mentioned in Chapter 4 it is necessary to ensure that the filter bandwidth is tailored to the type of transmission being received. It should be sufficient to ensure that all the signal can pass through the filter, but not so wide that off-channel interference is allowed through. As different types of transmission occupy different bandwidths this means that a variety of filters may be needed.

Particularly on scanners this function is achieved automatically dependent upon the type of transmission in use. However for communications receivers with several filters it is normally possible to select the filter needed. This allows the operator maximum flexibility to overcome any difficult reception conditions which may exist.

B.F.O.

On many sets there will be an adjustment for the b.f.o. It is required because the frequency of the oscillator needs to be varied according to the transmission being received. As described in Chapter 6 the signal being received needs to be in the centre of the pass-band, the b.f.o. then needs to be adjusted to the correct frequency. Often this can be pre-adjusted according to the mode in use, and as a result in many sets it is linked to the mode switch. In other sets, particularly older communications receivers, and some World Band types of short wave portables, the b.f.o. pitch needs to be set manually. This can be accomplished by tuning the set for the optimum signal with the b.f.o. switched out, and then adjusting the pitch control to give the best reception. Once it is correctly adjusted then it should be left in place for that type of transmission.

Scanning Facilities

Scanners are a very fast growing breed of radio. They are tailored to meet modern day requirements, particularly for listening on frequencies above 30MHz. They also use the latest in microprocessor technology to give them a whole host of features and facilities. In view of this they have many controls which are not normally found on other types of receiver. However their operation is normally quite straightforward.

Probably the most obvious control which all scanners have is a keypad. This makes them stand out from other types of receiver which by and large do not have keypads.

The keypads have a variety of keys to give them the flexibility which is commonplace with today's sets. Obviously the numeric keys are used for entering frequency information or selecting the number of a channel. In addition to this there are a number of other keys used to control other functions in the set.

One of these functions is the Delay. It is used to govern the amount of time the scanner will stay on a frequency after a signal has disappeared. This facility can be used when a station makes a number of short transmissions in quick succession before staying off the air for a longer time. By using the delay the scanner can be made to catch all the transmissions and then move on once they have finished.

The Enter and Memory keys are virtually self-explanatory. They are used for entering different frequencies into the memory and then recalling them later as required.

The Lock-out facility is used to prevent particular channels from being scanned. It may be that one channel in a scan is occupied with a transmission that is not of any interest. Alternatively it may have a high level of interference. Under either of these circumstances the channel, or a number of channels, can be locked out to prevent the scanner from monitoring them.

Scanners and many other types of receiver will possess a squelch control. This is used to mute or switch off the audio when no signals are present. This is particular useful for f.m. because high levels of background noise are present when no signal is present. The squelch control should be adjusted so that it just does not allow the audio to come on when there is no station on channel. By adjusting it like this even the weakest signals can be heard.

Location

Choosing a position for a radio is another important factor in its operation. For any radio there are a number of requirements. Ideally it should be kept away from damp and temperature extremes. Either of these will reduce the reliability of the set.

The radio should also be kept in a clean environment if at all possible. Dust and dirt will tend to build up in the set and particularly affect electromechanical items such as switches, volume controls and the like. Radios found in kitchens also suffer from switch problems caused by grease build-up on the switch contacts as a result of cooking.

Other aspects of locating a radio which are very important for the scanner or short wave listener are associated with the ease of operation. Ideally a convenient place should be found, preferably with a desk or table top to space out books, lists and any other paperwork which may be required. Tuning the set is also made easier because it is possible to rest the arm on the desk whilst using the controls.

Again for short wave receivers and scanners it is helpful to place them where they are unlikely to disturb other people in the house. This will also mean that other noises in the house are less likely to interrupt one's listening – quite an important factor when an interesting station has just been picked up.

If some of these points are borne in mind when settling on a place for the set then operating it will be much more convenient and more pleasurable.

Index